CAVITATION IN REAL LIQUIDS

SIR GEOFFREY TAYLOR
To whom this book is humbly dedicated

CAVITATION
IN REAL LIQUIDS

PROCEEDINGS OF THE SYMPOSIUM ON
CAVITATION IN REAL LIQUIDS,
GENERAL MOTORS RESEARCH LABORATORIES
WARREN, MICHIGAN, 1962

Edited by

ROBERT DAVIES
General Motors Research Laboratories,
Warren, Mich. (U.S.A.)

ELSEVIER PUBLISHING COMPANY
AMSTERDAM – LONDON – NEW YORK
1964

ELSEVIER PUBLISHING COMPANY
335 JAN VAN GALENSTRAAT, P.O. BOX 211, AMSTERDAM

AMERICAN ELSEVIER PUBLISHING COMPANY, INC.
52 VANDERBILT AVENUE, NEW YORK, N.Y. 10017

ELSEVIER PUBLISHING COMPANY LIMITED
12B, RIPPLESIDE COMMERCIAL ESTATE
RIPPLE ROAD, BARKING, ESSEX

LIBRARY OF CONGRESS CATALOG CARD NUMBER 63-22064

WITH 77 ILLUSTRATIONS AND 6 TABLES

List of Contributors

GARRETT BIRKHOFF, *Department of Mathematics, Harvard University, Cambridge, Mass.* (U.S.A.)

T. BROOKE BENJAMIN, *Department of Engineering, University of Cambridge* (England)

JAMES B. FEITEN, *Mechanical Development Department, General Motors Research Laboratories, Warren, Mich.* (U.S.A.)

LEIF FLOBERG, *Mechanical Engineering Department, Lund Institute of Technology* (Sweden)

P. R. GARABEDIAN, *Institute of Mathematical Sciences, New York University* (U.S.A.)

DONALD F. HAYS, *Mechanical Development Department, General Motors Research Laboratories, Warren, Mich.* (U.S.A.)

JOSEPH B. KELLER, *Courant Institute of Mathematical Sciences, New York University* (U.S.A.)

MILTON S. PLESSET, *Division of Engineering, California Institute of Technology, Pasadena, Calif.* (U.S.A.)

I. PRIGOGINE, *Faculté des Sciences, University of Brussels* (Belgium)

G. I. TAYLOR, *University of Cambridge* (England)

MARSHALL P. TULIN, *Hydronautics, Inc., Laurel, Md.* (U.S.A.)

J. W. WESTWATER, *Department of Chemistry and Chemical Engineering, University of Illinois, Urbana, Ill.* (U.S.A.)

List of Symposia

held at General Motors Research Laboratories
published by Elsevier Publishing Company, Amsterdam

1957. *Friction and Wear* (edited by ROBERT DAVIES), published 1959.

1958. *Internal Stresses and Fatigue in Metals* (edited by GERALD M. RASSWEILER and WILLIAM L. GRUBE), published 1959.

1959. *Theory of Traffic Flow* (edited by ROBERT HERMAN), published 1961.

1960. *Rolling Contact Phenomena* (edited by JOSEPH D. BIDWELL), published 1962.

1961. *Adhesion and Cohesion* (edited by PHILIP WEISS), published 1962.

1962. *Cavitation in Real Liquids* (edited by ROBERT DAVIES), this volume.

1963. *Liquids: Structure, Properties, Solid Interactions* (edited by THOMAS J. HUGHEL), to appear.

Preface

Cavities occur in almost every liquid of interest to man—and even in man himself. Their ubiquitous occurrence causes widespread concern over the need for a better understanding of the phenomenon among scientists and those in scientifically based professions. Physicists, for example, are interested in the nature of the interface between the two phases, mathematicians consider the conditions under which a free-boundary value problem is well-set, and applied engineers want to control cavitation damage.

The wide diversity of interest among those who are concerned with cavitation leads to a rich variety of literature, but the reader is lost in a maze of technical languages with little common vocabulary. Obviously there is a need to bring together these different contributions and points of view; the cavity itself is not so diverse.

More than a decade ago A. F. UNDERWOOD proposed that annually the General Motors Research Laboratories bring together scientists who are interested in a common subject but who may have different backgrounds. For the sixth such symposium, it seemed appropriate to concentrate on the theory of cavitation in real liquids. The Symposium was held in Warren, Michigan on September 24 and 25, 1962, and these proceedings are the papers presented at that meeting.

It is not possible to thank personally, or even to name, each of the one hundred or more people who organized and executed the Symposium. Nevertheless, mention should be made of GREGORY FLYNN who, as head of the sponsoring department, supported energetically and enthusiastically both the General Motors research reported herein and also the Symposium itself. The Symposium was considerably enriched by the stimulation and contributions of the individual speakers, chairmen, discussors, and other participants. To these many people go the appreciation of the General Motors Corporation and my own sincere personal thanks.

ROBERT DAVIES

Contents

Bubble Dynamics

MILTON S. PLESSET

*Division of Engineering, California Institute of Technology,
Pasadena, California*

INTRODUCTION

One of the earliest precise formulations of a problem in bubble dynamics must surely be that made by BESANT in his *Hydrostatics and Hydrodynamics* in 1859. The problem was stated in the following way:

'An infinite mass of homogeneous incompressible fluid acted upon by no forces is at rest, and a spherical portion of the fluid is suddenly annihilated; it is required to find the instantaneous alteration of pressure at any point of the mass, and the time in which the cavity will be filled up, the pressure at an infinite distance being supposed to remain constant.' As we know, RAYLEIGH[1] presumably having become interested in the problem of cavitation and cavitation damage, gave an elegant solution for this problem. In addition, Rayleigh considered the motion of a bubble containing a permanent gas which he assumed to be isothermal. We propose to present here some of the developments of the theory which have been made in recent years in the Besant-Rayleigh problem, and in particular we propose to examine the assumptions and simplifications introduced in the theory so that we can determine how useful the results of the calculations will be. In our discussion we shall emphasize as far as possible the physical, rather than the mathematical, aspects of the problems. We do this not because we believe that the physics of this field is more interesting or important than the mathematics but because others are much better able to consider the mathematical side and also because we are primarily concerned with the applicability of the results of the theory to experiment or to engineering problems.

To formulate the problem of bubble dynamics we have at our disposal the three fundamental conservation laws of continuum mechanics. These are, of course, the conservation laws of mass, momentum, and energy which are to be applied both in the gaseous as well as the liquid phase. Since bubbles often grow in a liquid from submicroscopic 'nuclei', there might be some question of the applicability

of the laws of continuum mechanics in their conventional form to the behavior
in the 'nuclear' range. It must be confessed that there are many aspects of the
behavior of nuclei which are not yet clear and these will be touched upon later, but
it appears reasonable to say that these nuclei are large enough so that the laws
of continuum mechanics may be applied. For most of the present discussion any
lack of knowledge about the properties of these nuclei does not lead to a significant
limitation of the applicability of our results to experiment.

In addition to the conservation laws we need equations of state for both phases.
We may indicate here limiting conditions which are often of help in simplifying
the problem. We have one condition in which the bubble contains essentially no
permanent gas. In this case we say that we have a vapor bubble; or, as it is sometimes expressed, we say that we have 'vaporous cavitation'. The case, in which
the amount of permanent gas greatly exceeds the amount of vapor, is of course
the case of a gas bubble, or of 'gaseous cavitation'. We may note at this point the
static behavior of a gas bubble and a vapor bubble; in both cases, surface tension
is involved. If there is a pressure balance between the pressure p' within the bubble
and a pressure p outside so that

$$p' = p + 2\sigma/R$$

where R is the bubble radius and σ is the surface tension, then this balance is
unstable for a vapor bubble in the sense that a slight increase in the bubble size
leads to further growth and a slight decrease to collapse of the bubble. This growth
is driven by the decrease in the surface tension force, $2\sigma/R$. There is a different
instability in the static gas bubble[2]. Even though the liquid is saturated with
dissolved gas corresponding to a liquid pressure p, the bubble will dissolve by mass
diffusion of gas out of the bubble into the liquid. This dissolution by diffusion is
again driven by surface tension. It is just this behavior which leads to a question
regarding the stability of the nuclei in a liquid. It is known that liquids will not
withstand very large tensions unless they have been given special treatment so
that the nuclei, or holes, in the liquid have sizes equivalent to spheres of 10^{-3}
cm to perhaps 10^{-5} cm in radius. The effect of surface tension must be neutralized
in some way so that these nuclei can persist. One might suppose that this is accomplished by the nuclei being stabilized on solid particles. We know that the
presence of a solid surface makes it possible for a gas phase in a liquid to have a
vanishing surface energy. I shall not go into the experiments which have been
performed in the past and which give some information regarding nuclei but I
would like to remark that further experimentation seems desirable.

We are primarily concerned here with the dynamic behavior of bubbles so that
static stability questions are therefore not of concern. Ambiguities regarding
nuclei do mean, however, that results which depend closely on the parameters

of the nuclei will not be definite. We shall see that these limitations are not significant for many problems.

We return to the final aspect of the formulation of the problem as a problem in continuum mechanics. In addition to any pertinent initial conditions, we must consider boundary conditions. We shall include this aspect of the formulation of the problem separately for vapor bubbles and for gas bubbles. While there are many common features for both kinds of bubbles, it is helpful to be specific at this point since it is then easier to emphasize the physical features of the different problems. In all our discussion we shall suppose that the external conditions are such that there is no tendency to disturb spherical symmetry. Therefore, we shall be considering problems in which the acceleration of gravity may be neglected. There are some other presentations at this symposium which will examine conditions under which gravity may not be neglected. Even under the assumption of spherical symmetry in the conditions of the problem we shall see that there is the possibility of dynamic instability which will deform a bubble from a spherical shape.

DYNAMICS OF VAPOR BUBBLES

In order that vapor bubbles not contain appreciable amounts of a permanent gas, it is necessary that they grow from the small initial size of the nucleus to macroscopic dimensions in a short time. Otherwise dissolved gas in the liquid will diffuse into the bubble and affect the dynamics. While the nucleus may be expected to contain a significant amount of permanent gases which will be the same presumably as the dissolved gases, the effect of such a quantity of permanent gas will become negligible very early in the bubble growth, certainly by the time the bubble size has increased by one order of magnitude beyond the nucleus size.

We may now distinguish two kinds of vapor bubbles depending on the liquid temperature under which they grow. The first kind may be called cavitation bubbles and is the kind which grows in a liquid which is at a temperature sufficiently low so that the latent heat requirement for evaporation of the vapor may be neglected. Under this condition the pressure within the bubble, p', remains nearly constant so that the growth problem is fairly simple[3]. We can justify this thermal behavior in the following way. Let the bubble grow from a negligible initial radius and from rest to a radius R in a time t. The growth velocity of the bubble $\dot{R}$ is always bounded. The total mass of vapor evaporated into the bubble is $(4\pi/3)R^3\varrho'$ where ϱ' is the vapor density. The total heat requirement is

$$Q = \frac{4\pi}{3} R^3\varrho'L$$

where L is the latent heat of evaporation. This heat flows into the bubble from a layer of liquid surrounding the bubble which has a thickness which is given by $(Dt)^{\frac{1}{2}}$ where D is the thermal diffusivity of the liquid. The temperature drop, ΔT, through this layer of liquid is determined by the relation

$$\frac{4\pi}{3} R^3 \varrho' L \simeq 4\pi R^2 (Dt)^{\frac{1}{2}} \varrho c \Delta T;$$

$$\Delta T \simeq \frac{R}{3} \frac{\varrho' L}{\varrho c} \frac{1}{(Dt)^{\frac{1}{2}}}.$$

If we take, as an example, a cavitation bubble in water at $15°$ C we have $\varrho'/\varrho \sim 10^{-5}$, $L/c \sim 600$, and $D = 1.41 \times 10^{-3}$ cm²/sec. Since a cavitation bubble will typically grow to a few millimeters in radius in a few milliseconds, we see that the temperature drop is only a fraction of a degree. We recall from the general behavior of the vapor pressure as a function of temperature that the rate of change of vapor pressure with temperature is rather small for temperatures well below the boiling point of the liquid. It follows that the vapor pressure will not change greatly during the course of the bubble growth. The heat equation, or the energy equation, therefore does not enter into the problem of the growth of a vapor bubble in a cool liquid. The growth process we may say is dominated by inertial effects. Since the heat flow effects are not important, we need not be concerned with the thermal boundary conditions. We must, however, consider the condition of stress continuity across the interface. This condition is

$$p' = p(R) + \frac{2\sigma}{R} + 4\mu \frac{\dot{R}}{R}$$

where $p' = p_v(T)$, the vapor pressure, $p(R)$ is the pressure in the liquid at the bubble wall, σ is the surface tension, and μ is the coefficient of viscosity. If we take the flow to be irrotational, and if we neglect the compressibility of the liquid, we then have a Bernoulli integral of the momentum equation. From this equation, applied to the bubble boundary, we find that the velocity of the bubble wall approaches for large R the value

$$\dot{R} \simeq \left[\frac{2(p_v - P_0)}{3\varrho} \right]^{\frac{1}{2}}$$

where P_0 is the pressure in the liquid at infinity (assumed constant here). This upper bound on the growth velocity usually represents a moderate value compared, for example, with the sound velocity in the vapor or in the liquid. As a consequence, the pressure in the vapor p' can be taken as the equilibrium vapor pressure. It is not obvious that such need be the case since evaporation, or con-

References p. 17–18

densation, is a process which takes place at a finite rate. The characteristic velocity for either of these processes is[4]

$$c^* = \frac{\alpha c}{(2\pi\gamma)^{\frac{1}{2}}}$$

where c is the sound velocity in the vapor, γ is the ratio of specific heats, and α is the accommodation coefficient. For a liquid-vapor interface velocity, $\dot{R}$, away from the vapor pressure in the vapor, p', is related to the equilibrium vapor pressure p_v as follows:

$$\frac{p'}{p_v} = \frac{c^*}{c^* + \dot{R}} .$$

It appears that the accommodation coefficient for water is rather small as might perhaps be expected. The accommodation coefficient measures the probability that a vapor molecule will stick to the liquid surface upon striking it. The water molecule is polar and of course rather unsymmetrical so that α could very well be a small number. It has been measured for water at $0°$ C and found to be 0.04 which gives $c^* = 8$ m/sec. This is a rather low velocity and there is some indirect evidence that α is somewhat larger than 0.04 at higher temperatures.

A remark may be made regarding a particular aspect of the condition of conservation of mass for vapor bubbles. Because of evaporation, or condensation, the velocity of the interface, $\dot{R}$, does not coincide with the velocity of the liquid, $v(R)$, adjacent to the interface. If $v'(R)$ is the velocity of the vapor adjacent to the interface, then our conservation condition gives

$$\varrho'(v' - \dot{R}) = \varrho(v - \dot{R})$$

where ϱ' is the vapor density and ϱ the liquid density. Then we have

$$v = \dot{R}\left[1 - \frac{\varrho'}{\varrho}\left(1 - \frac{v'}{\dot{R}}\right)\right]$$

and it is evident that $v(R)$ is very nearly equal to $\dot{R}$ because $\varrho'/\varrho \sim 10^{-5}$.

We may now turn our attention to the collapse of a vapor bubble. The situation of physical interest again corresponds to the cold liquid; that is, a liquid at a temperature well below the boiling temperature. So long as the collapse velocity, $\dot{R}$, remains moderate our conclusion that the heat flow may be neglected remains valid. In contrast to the growth for which $\dot{R}$ remained bounded, for collapse $\dot{R}$ eventually increases, and without limit. If we suppose that the pressure at infinity, P_0, remains constant as well as the pressure, p', within the bubble, we may write from the Bernoulli equation

$$\dot{R}^2 \cong \frac{2}{3\varrho} (P_0 - p') \left(\frac{R_0{}^3}{R^3} - 1 \right)$$

where R_0 is the initial radius of the bubble and where, in addition, we have neglected surface tension and viscosity. For typical cases we find that $\dot{R}$ remains sufficiently small so that thermal effects can be neglected until the bubble radius has decreased by a factor of 10 or more. In this range, and for the entire range of growth, thermal effects are unimportant. As R decreases further and $\dot{R}$ increases, it is evident that we should be concerned about several effects in addition to the heating of the bubble by condensation. We might expect surface tension effects and viscous effects to become significant. Actually for bubbles with initial radius, R_0, of 1 mm or more, neglect of surface tension and viscous effects introduces an error which is less than 1% up to the point at which the bubble radius has decreased to $R \sim 10^{-3}$ mm (this figure has been determined by calculation for collapsing pressure $P_0 - p' \geq 0.3$ atm). Compressibility of the liquid is an effect which is important much earlier in the collapse history. Theoretical analysis by GILMORE[5] shows that the collapse velocity $\dot{R}$ becomes infinite as R approaches zero although it does so less strongly than $R^{-\frac{3}{2}}$ which is the result of the incompressible solution written above. We may remark, however, that the thermal effects are important before any of these other effects become significant. This thermal heating of the bubble arises first from the heat of condensation and second from the fact that the condensation eventually cannot keep up with the interface motion. The vapor then is heated by compression like a permanent gas.

This description of the collapse will, as we shall see below, have to be modified because the spherical shape of the collapsing bubble becomes unstable and the bubble will break up as a consequence. It will therefore be evident that the collapse history of a cavitation bubble does not proceed into the region of extremely complicated behavior in which the bubble heating, liquid compressibility, and an involved change in the equations of state of the vapor and the liquid must be considered.

We may now consider a vapor bubble at a liquid temperature in the neighborhood of the boiling point. For the cavitation bubble growth just discussed the tension on the liquid $P_0 - p_v$ is usually large compared with p_v, and minor variations in p_v in the course of the growth are unimportant. For boiling bubbles, as we shall denote them, the variations in p_v which result from latent heat requirements become decisive. The growth of such vapor bubbles is controlled not by inertial effects but by thermal effects. We must, therefore, expect large deviations from the behavior predicted by the Rayleigh solution. We may deduce this behavior after the bubble has grown somewhat beyond the nuclear size by a simple argument based on thermal considerations. In a boiling bubble the tempera-

References p. 17–18

ture difference between the liquid at the bubble wall and that at a distance is only slightly less than $T_0 - T_b$ where T_0 is the temperature in the 'superheated' liquid at a distance, and T_b is the temperature at which the vapor pressure equals the ambient pressure. The temperature drop in the liquid takes place in a liquid layer around the bubble of approximate thickness given by the diffusion length $(Dt)^{\frac{1}{2}}$. The heat flow per unit time into the bubble is therefore given approximately by

$$\dot{Q} \simeq 4\pi R^2 k \frac{(T_0 - T_b)}{(Dt)^{\frac{1}{2}}}$$

where k is the thermal conductivity of the liquid. The heat requirement per unit time for evaporation, on the other hand, is

$$\dot{Q} = L \frac{\mathrm{d}}{\mathrm{d}t} \left(\frac{4\pi}{3} R^3 \varrho' \right) \simeq 4\pi R^2 \dot{R} L \varrho'.$$

The approximation indicated in this last equation is based on the fact that the heat flow requirement because of the volume change is considerably greater than that arising from the relatively small change in vapor density. From these two equations, we obtain

$$\dot{R} \simeq \frac{k}{L\varrho'} \frac{(T_0 - T_b)}{(Dt)^{\frac{1}{2}}}.$$

An accurate calculation[6] gives this same result with an additional factor $(\pi/3)^{\frac{1}{2}}$. It should be remarked that the thermal diffusivity in the vapor is usually much larger than that of the liquid. The diffusion length in the vapor is then large enough so that one need not be concerned with variations in temperature or density within the bubble.

These are common features in the dynamics of cavitation and boiling bubbles. The inertial effects of the vapor may be neglected. For the growth problem, surface tension is important only in the early or nuclear stage. Viscosity is unimportant as is the compressibility of the liquid. For the collapse of a vapor bubble, one might expect compressibility effects in the liquid as well as surface tension and viscosity to become important toward the end of the collapse. As we shall see, instability in the bubble shape causes the bubble to break up before these complications can strongly affect the bubble dynamics in the final stage of collapse.

DYNAMICS OF GAS BUBBLES

Thermodynamics of Bubble Oscillations

The behavior of gas bubbles in a static pressure field and the growth or dissolution by mass diffusion under this condition has already been mentioned. This diffusion is a slow process and will be neglected for the present. We shall discuss now the behavior of an oscillating bubble. In particular, if the effects of heat conduction are ignored, the oscillating bubble problem reduces to the problem considered over a hundred years ago by Besant. If we wish to include heat flow, the problem becomes more complex and also more realistic. In order to determine the behavior we linearize the problem. In addition we suppose that the conditions within the bubble are spatially uniform. We shall return later to the discussion of the conditions within the gas. With these simplifications, we have as would be expected a problem equivalent to a harmonic oscillator with heat conduction as the mechanism.

We let ω denote the angular frequency, k_L the thermal conductivity of the liquid, and k_g the thermal conductivity of the gas of which the bubble is composed. The thermal diffusivity of the liquid, D_L, and that of the gas, D_g, are given by

$$D_L = \frac{k_L}{\varrho_L c_L} = \frac{k_L}{C_L}; \qquad D_g = \frac{k_g}{\varrho_g c_g} = \frac{k_g}{C_g};$$

where c_L and c_g are specific heats per unit mass at constant volume, and C_L and C_g are specific heats per unit volume. We also denote the equilibrium radius of the bubble by R_0 and the heat diffusion lengths in the liquid and in the gas by Λ_L and Λ_g, respectively, where

$$\Lambda_L = (D_L/\omega)^{\frac{1}{2}}; \quad \Lambda_g = (D_g/\omega)^{\frac{1}{2}}.$$

Then our linearized solution[7] shows that the average behavior of the bubble is

$$\text{isothermal if } \frac{C_L \Lambda_L}{C_g R_0} \gg 1,$$

and

$$\text{adiabatic if } \frac{C_L \Lambda_L}{C_g R_0} \ll 1.$$

These results are physically entirely reasonable. For, the larger the ratio C_L/C_g, the larger is the capacity of the liquid to absorb heat relative to that of the gas; at the same time the region in the liquid over which this heat is absorbed increases with Λ_L.

The physical argument for this behavior may be given very simply as follows. The increase in internal energy of the bubble for an increment in temperature ΔT is

$$\Delta h_g \cong \tfrac{4}{3}\pi R_0^3 C_g \Delta T.$$

On the other hand, the flow of heat from the liquid during, for example, the compression half-cycle is

$$\Delta h_{\rm L} \simeq k_{\rm L} \frac{\Delta T}{\Lambda_{\rm L}} 4\pi R_0{}^2 \frac{\pi}{\omega} .$$

We find, therefore,

$$\frac{\Delta h_{\rm L}}{\Delta h_{\rm g}} \simeq 3\pi \frac{C_{\rm L}}{C_{\rm g}} \frac{\Lambda_{\rm L}}{R_0} .$$

Now if $\Delta h_{\rm g} \ll \Delta h_{\rm L}$, then only an insignificant part of the transferred heat energy is available for increase of the internal energy, or equivalently for raising the bubble temperature. This situation is one in which the heat diffusion is so rapid that temperature changes do not take place. The thermodynamic process is thus essentially isothermal. On the other hand, if $\Delta h_{\rm g} \gg \Delta h_{\rm L}$, the corresponding argument leads to the expectation that the bubble behavior would be adiabatic. These are just the results which are obtained from the detailed analysis if the assumption is made that the temperature within the bubble is uniform.

We may rewrite our thermodynamic criterion so that the frequency dependence is contained in the diffusion length for the gas rather than in the diffusion length for the liquid:

$$\frac{C_{\rm L}}{C_{\rm g}} \frac{\Lambda_{\rm L}}{R_0} = \frac{C_{\rm L}}{C_{\rm g}} \left(\frac{D_{\rm L}}{D_{\rm g}} \right)^{\frac{1}{2}} \frac{\Lambda_{\rm g}}{R_0} .$$

We may note that the coefficient of $\Lambda_{\rm g}/R_0$ in this last expression is usually large compared with unity; for an air bubble in water $(C_{\rm L}/C_{\rm g}) (D_{\rm L}/D_{\rm g})^{\frac{1}{2}} \sim 300$. It follows that we have the isothermal condition when $\Lambda_{\rm g} > R_0$. In addition, we then know from this comparison of $\Lambda_{\rm g}$ with R_0 that the temperature in the bubble will be uniform so that the model used in the analysis will be accurate. On the other hand, at higher frequencies which make $\Lambda_{\rm g} < R_0$, the temperature within the bubble cannot be uniform, and the model used in the analysis is not accurate. On physical grounds, however, we know that in this case the bubble behavior will be adiabatic.

From the dependence of $\Lambda_{\rm g}$, or $\Lambda_{\rm L}$, on ω, which leads to the isothermal behavior at low frequencies and to the adiabatic behavior at high frequencies, we might interpret these results as showing that for a slow process there is sufficient time for heat to be conducted away so as to maintain the isothermal condition in the bubble and that for a fast process there is not sufficient time for heat conduction so as to give the adiabatic condition. This reasoning is not correct as we shall now see. The bubble problem may be solved when the requirement is no longer imposed that conditions are uniform throughout the bubble. The analytic results[7] are of such complexity that it is difficult to obtain physical conclusions regarding details of the process. To determine the thermodynamic behavior, averages both over time and over the bubble interior are sufficient. One then finds the following limiting behavior for the ratio of the internal energy increase of the bubble to the heat absorbed:

$$\frac{\Delta h_g}{\delta Q} \simeq O(\omega), \quad \text{as} \quad \omega \to 0;$$

and

$$\frac{\Delta h_g}{\delta Q} \simeq \left(\frac{k_g C_g}{k_L C_L}\right)^{\frac{1}{2}}, \quad \text{as} \quad \omega \to \infty.$$

The low frequency behavior is isothermal which is the same result as was found with the uniform bubble approximation. The high frequency limit would be adiabatic only if $(k_g C_g/k_L C_L)^{\frac{1}{2}}$ is a large number. This quantity, however, is usually quite small; for an air bubble in water, we have

$$\left(\frac{k_g C_g}{k_L C_L}\right)^{\frac{1}{2}} \simeq 10^{-3}$$

so that the very high frequency limit is also isothermal.

In order to determine the approximate behavior between these limits we have recourse to physical arguments. We know that the bubble oscillations will be isothermal in the low frequency range for which $R_0 < \Lambda_g < \lambda_g$. As the frequency is increased so that $\Lambda_g < R_0 < \lambda_g$, we expect the bubble oscillations to be adiabatic. If now we consider frequencies so high that $\lambda_g < R_0$, we make use of a different physical picture of the process. If the wavelength of the oscillations in the bubble, λ_g, is small compared with the bubble size, then the effect of the surrounding liquid cannot be significant for the bubble interior. The thermodynamic behavior of the gas bubble may then be determined just as it would be for a homogeneous medium. For a homogeneous medium, the oscillations are adiabatic if $\Lambda_g/\lambda_g < 1$, and they are isothermal if $\Lambda_g/\lambda_g > 1$. We see that we get the isothermal limit at very high frequencies in agreement with the more complete theoretical model, and the adiabatic behavior at lower frequencies. The thermodynamic behavior is summarized in Table I, and numerical values are given in Table IA. It is perhaps unnecessary to add that the adiabatic behavior indicated between the two isothermal limits is approximate only.

Rectified Diffusion

We have just considered first order effects in gas bubble oscillations with our interest centered on the thermodynamics. We shall now consider a second order effect which involves mass transport of gas dissolved in the liquid into the bubble. This mass transport is called rectified diffusion, which is given this name because

TABLE I

THERMODYNAMIC BEHAVIOR OF AN OSCILLATING GAS BUBBLE IN LIQUID

Frequency Range	Comparison of Lengths	Relevant Criterion	Thermodynamic Behavior
Very High	$\lambda_g \ll \Lambda_g \ll R_0$	$\dfrac{\Lambda_g}{\lambda_g} \gg 1$	Isothermal
High	$\Lambda_g < \lambda_g < R_0$	$\dfrac{\Lambda_g}{\lambda_g} < 1$	Adiabatic
Moderately High	$\Lambda_g < R_0 < \lambda_g$	$\dfrac{\Lambda_g}{R_0} < 1$	Adiabatic
Low	$R_0 < \Lambda_g < \lambda_g$	$\dfrac{C'_L \Lambda_L}{C'_g R_0} \gg 1$	Isothermal

TABLE IA

AIR BUBBLE IN WATER

$(D_g \simeq 0.3$ cm²/sec.$)$

	$R_0 = 10^{-5}$ cm	10^{-4}	10^{-3}	10^{-2}	10^{-1}	
$\lambda_g < \Lambda_g < R_0$	$\nu > 3 \times 10^9$ c/s	$> 3 \times 10^9$	$> 3 \times 10^9$	$> 3 \times 10^9$	$> 3 \times 10^9$	Isothermal
$\Lambda_g = \lambda_g < R_0$	$\nu = 3 \times 10^9$ c/s	3×10^9	3×10^9	3×10^9	3×10^9	Transition Range
$\Lambda_g < \lambda_g < R_0$			3×10^8	10^8	3×10^7	Adiabatic
$\Lambda_g < R_0 = \lambda_g$	3×10^9	3×10^8	3×10^7	3×10^6	3×10^5	
$\Lambda_g < R_0 < \lambda_g$			3×10^6	10^5	3×10^3	Adiabatic
$R_0 = \Lambda_g < \lambda_g$	3×10^9	3×10^7	3×10^5	3×10^3	3×10	Transition Range
$R_0 < \Lambda_g < \lambda_g$	$\nu < 3 \times 10^9$ c/s	$< 3 \times 10^7$	$< 3 \times 10^5$	$< 3 \times 10^3$	$< 3 \times 10$	Isothermal

there is a net flow of gas into a bubble in a liquid saturated with dissolved gas when the liquid is subject to an oscillating pressure field. The process may be given the following physical explanation. When the pressure rises above its mean value, the gas bubble is compressed and at the same time the concentration of dissolved gas in the liquid is then below the equilibrium value appropriate for the increased pressure. This situation results in an outflow of gas from the bubble. On the other hand, by a corresponding argument, gas flows into the bubble from the liquid in its neighborhood during the expansion half-cycle. Because of the difference in surface area of the bubble between these two half-cycles, there will be a net gas flow into the bubble over a complete cycle. An approximate treatment of the effect purely on the basis of the area effect has been given and is in serious disagreement with experimental observations. We can readily see that this quasi-static approach makes a large error because it neglects the effect of convection in the mass diffusion equation, and the convection effect should be important

References p. 17–18

because the mass diffusion length in the liquid is usually small compared with the bubble radius. The analysis[8] indeed shows a large effect from convection, and the complete calculation gives

$$\frac{dm}{dt} = \frac{8\pi}{3} Dc_\infty R_0 \left(\frac{P_{max} - P_0}{P_0}\right)^2 [1 + O(\Lambda/R_0)].$$

Here Λ is the diffusion length, c_∞ is the dissolved concentration at a distance from the bubble, and R_0 is the equilibrium bubble radius corresponding to the mean pressure P_0.

This result applies to the situation in which the liquid is just saturated with dissolved gas at the equilibrium concentration c_∞ associated with the pressure P_0. If we consider the situation in which the dissolved concentration c_∞ is less than the equilibrium dissolved concentration for the pressure P_0 which we now denote by c_0, then the steady outward diffusion from the bubble in this undersaturated case is given by

$$\frac{dm'}{dt} = -4\pi DR_0 \left[c_0 \left(1 + \frac{2\sigma}{P_0 R_0}\right) - c_\infty\right]$$

where σ is the surface tension coefficient so that the pressure on the gas in the bubble is $P_0 + 2\sigma/R_0$. Now we may find the threshold oscillation pressure $P_{max} = P_t$ which is just sufficient to balance the rate of diffusion; i.e., which makes $dm/dt = dm'/dt$:

$$P_t = \left(\frac{3}{2}\right)^{\frac{1}{2}} P_0 \left(1 + \frac{2\sigma}{P_0 R_0} - \frac{c_\infty}{c_0}\right)^{\frac{1}{2}}.$$

Measurements have been made[9] of the threshold pressure peak, P_t, for various values, P_0, of the mean liquid pressure. A comparison[9] of observations with a calculation based on the area effect alone (Blake theory) and with the calculation including convection (Hsieh-Plesset theory) is shown in Table II.

TABLE II

THRESHOLDS FOR RECTIFIED DIFFUSION*

Static Pressure (atm)	Dissolved Concentration Ratio C_∞/C_0	Bubble Radius $(10^{-3}cm)$	Threshold Sound Pressure Peak (atm)		
			Strasberg's Measured Values	H-P Theory	Blake Theory
1.00	0.85	2.6	0.42	0.56	0.060
1.00	0.84	3.7	0.33	0.55	0.051
0.55	0.86	2.3	>0.21	0.31	0.037

* From STRASBERG[9].

A final remark should be made regarding the rectification rate for a bubble in a saturated solution. Our result for dm/dt shows that the bubble radius increases indefinitely in time like $t^{\frac{1}{2}}$. On the other hand it is known experimentally that the rectified growth of bubbles does not proceed indefinitely. Here again we encounter a stability effect. The general stability analysis now to be described explains the observation that there is an upper limit on bubble size growth in an oscillating pressure field.

BUBBLE STABILITY

We are concerned with the stability of the interface between two fluids of different densities which are accelerated in a direction normal to the interface. The problem for a plane interface has been solved by TAYLOR[10]. We may sketch the solution here. Let us suppose that the interface is $y = H(t)$ and that the fluid in the region $y > H$ has negligible density compared with the fluid in the region $y < H$. This interface is assumed to be disturbed into the form

$$y_s = H + a_k \cos kx$$

where $a_k(t)$ is taken to be a small quantity. The velocity potential is perturbed to

$$\varphi = \varphi_0 + \varphi_1$$

where

$$\varphi_0 = - \dot{H}y,$$

and

$$\varphi_1 = b_k e^{k(y-H)} \cos kx.$$

By application of the kinematic condition at $y = H$ which requires that

$$v_s = \frac{dy_s}{dt} = - \frac{\partial \varphi}{\partial y} = - \left(\frac{\partial \varphi_0}{\partial y} + \frac{\partial \varphi_1}{\partial y} \right),$$

we find that

$$\dot{a}_k = - kb_k.$$

We may satisfy the dynamic boundary condition at the interface by using the Bernoulli integral; we find in this way that

$$\ddot{H}a_k - \dot{b}_k = 0.$$

Our result is therefore

$$\ddot{a}_k + k\ddot{H}a_k = 0.$$

We find the Taylor result that, when the acceleration is directed from the heavy fluid to the light one ($\ddot{H} > 0$), the plane interface is stable and when the acceleration is directed from the light fluid to the heavy one ($\ddot{H} < 0$), the plane interface is unstable.

References p. 17–18

If the same results held for a gas or vapor bubble in a liquid, it would be difficult to understand how a gas nucleus accelerated into a macroscopic bubble could be spherical. Actually, we can show[11] that these results do not hold for a curved interface. We shall here consider a spherical bubble in a liquid. We do not affect the physical nature of the problem if we neglect the gas density relative to the liquid density. We consider the spherical interface $r = R(t)$ disturbed to the shape

$$r_s = R + aY_n$$

where Y_n is a spherical harmonic of degree n, and a is a small quantity. We suppose that the flow may be described in the gas region by a velocity potential, φ_1, and in the liquid region by a velocity potential φ_2. As for the plane case we have the kinematic boundary condition

$$- \left(\frac{\partial \varphi_1}{\partial r} \right)_{r_s} = - \left(\frac{\partial \varphi_2}{\partial r} \right)_{r_s} = \dot{R} + \dot{a}Y_n$$

The dynamic boundary condition is satisfied by using the Bernoulli equation to evaluate the pressure on either side of the interface; these pressures are then connected by the relation

$$p_2 = p_1 - \sigma \left(\frac{1}{R'} + \frac{1}{R''} \right)$$

where R' and R'' are the principle radii of curvature of the interface. In this way we find the equation for $n = 0$ for the unperturbed motion:

$$R\ddot{R} + \frac{3}{2}\dot{R}^2 = \frac{P_1 - P_2 - 2\sigma/R}{\varrho} \tag{1}$$

where ϱ is the liquid density, P_1 is the pressure within the bubble and P_2 the pressure in the liquid at $R = \infty$. The stability condition which we find for $n > 0$ is

$$\ddot{a} + \frac{3\dot{R}}{R}\dot{a} - Aa = 0, \tag{2}$$

where

$$A = \frac{(n-1)\ddot{R}}{R} - \frac{(n-1)(n+1)(n+2)\sigma}{\varrho R^3}. \tag{3}$$

When bubble expansion is driven by a pressure difference $P_1 - P_2 = P$ which approaches a constant as R increases so that $\dot{R}^2 \to 2P/3\varrho$, it is easy to show that

$$a \to \text{const.}, \quad \text{as} \quad R \to \infty$$

and consequently that

References p. 17–18

$$\frac{a}{R} \to 0, \qquad R \to \infty .$$

If we consider a collapsing bubble and suppose that $p = P_2 - P_1$ remains positive as R decreases, we can readily find that

$$a \sim R^{-\frac{1}{4}} \exp\left[\pm icn^{\frac{1}{2}} \int^t R^{-\frac{5}{2}} dt'\right], \qquad R \to 0,$$

where c is positive, being proportional to p and n is the order of the spherical harmonic $(n > 1)$ associated with a. We see from these results that the stability behavior for the plane interface is not applicable to the spherical interface. The growth of the spherical interface is stable and the collapse is unstable. Further, the instability of the collapse is qualitatively unaffected by surface tension. A detailed study[12] has been made of the behavior of $a(t)$ for the case in which $P_1 - P_2$ is constant. These more extensive results, of course, agree with the conclusions just stated. We find, in particular, that the instability on collapse already becomes very evident when the radius has been reduced to about 1/10 of its initial value. This finding is of importance since it is the basis for our previous remark that instability in the collapse of a vapor bubble becomes important before the effects of compressibility, viscosity, surface tension, or heat conduction become very large.

We shall not consider here a general unperturbed motion and the corresponding stability criteria for $a(t)$. As we might expect, the behavior just described gives the essential results. It may, however, be of interest to remark that one may show that fluid compressibility does not have a significant effect on the behavior of the Taylor instability.

For bubbles which contain very small amounts of permanent gas we see that the decrease in bubble size during collapse proceeds far enough so that there is a fragmentation of the original bubble. This effect together with the disappearance of the differences between the liquid and the vapor phase presumably explains the experimental observation that the reopening of a cavity often does not occur with the reversal of the liquid motion. We should also remark that the arrest of the liquid motion can be expected to produce a sharp pressure pulse which will radiate from the collapse point. Here we have, of course, a compressibility effect although the pressure pulse can be treated like a weak shock because of the special compressibility properties of liquids. This approximation is a good one even for intense pressure pulses. For bubbles, on the other hand, which contain appreciable amounts of permanent gas, the decrease in bubble size may not proceed far enough to develop large instabilities. The experimental observations in this situation of 'gaseous cavitation' are that bubble rebound occurs and that the acoustic radiation is much less intense than for 'vaporous cavitation'.

A question which remains concerns the stability of a gas bubble in an oscillating pressure field. The equation for the unperturbed motion in this case (*cf.* eqn. (1)) has the external pressure

$$P_2 = P_0(1 + \varepsilon \sin \omega t)$$

and, when ε is small compared with unity, a linearized calculation gives the solution for R as

$$R = R_0[1 + \delta \sin (\omega t + \varphi)]. \tag{4}$$

The quantity δ is of the same order of magnitude as ε, and φ is a constant phase shift which for convenience may be put equal to zero. The stability equation (2) may be transformed by the substitution

$$b = R^{\frac{3}{2}}a$$

which puts it in the form

$$\ddot{b} + G(t)b = 0. \tag{5}$$

A straightforward calculation[8] shows that $G(t)$ has the form

$$G(t) = \alpha + \beta \sin \omega t \tag{6}$$

where

$$\alpha = \frac{(n - 1)(n + 1)(n + 2)\sigma}{\varrho R_0^3} + O(\delta^2), \tag{7}$$

$$\beta = \delta\{(n + \tfrac{1}{2})\omega^2 - (n - 1)(n + 1)(n + 2)(3\sigma/\varrho R_0^3)\} + O(\delta^2). \tag{8}$$

Our stability equation (5) is just the Mathieu equation. The stability theory of solutions of the Mathieu equation is well known. We may, however, see in very simple terms that the solution is essentially unstable if $G < 0$. In applying this criterion to eqn. (7), we must keep in mind that the values of n of interest do not include $n = 1$ since this value of n corresponds not to a distortion of the spherical shape but to a translation of the entire bubble. From the forms of α and β one may see that the greater n the greater is the limit of stability. Therefore for the determination of the critical radius it is sufficient to consider only the case $n = 2$. We then find that eqn. (6) gives

$$G(t) = \frac{12\,\sigma}{\varrho R_0^3} + \delta \left[\frac{5}{2}\omega^2 - \frac{36\,\sigma}{\varrho R_0^3}\right] \sin \omega t.$$

An order of magnitude criterion of stability is thus

$$\frac{12\,\sigma}{\varrho R^3} \gtrsim \frac{5}{2}\delta\omega^2$$

from which we get

$$(R_0)_{cr} \sim \left[\frac{24}{5} \frac{\sigma}{\varrho \delta \omega^2}\right]^{\frac{1}{2}} .$$

Let us illustrate this result by considering the case of an air bubble in water. We then have $\sigma = 73$ dyne/cm and $\varrho = 1$ gm/cm^3. We take the example of $\delta = 10^{-2}$ and $\omega = 10^4$/sec, and we get

$$(R_0)_{cr} \sim \tfrac{1}{10} \text{ cm.}$$

This value furnishes a most reasonable upper limit on the stable size of an oscillating bubble.

CONCLUSION

The problem of rectified diffusion is certainly a problem in bubble dynamics which has been treated in the spirit of Besant and Rayleigh. The only added features are that it is a process of second order in the oscillating pressure amplitude and that mass transport from the one phase to the other must be included. For the remaining problems which have been discussed here the new physical aspects which distinguish them from the approach of one hundred years ago are either the thermodynamics or the stability of vapor and gas bubble dynamics. The methods which are used for the analysis are, however, entirely classical.

We may note some problems in bubble dynamics which need further analysis. It is clear that as soon as we lose complete spherical symmetry, the added complexity of more than one space variable almost always puts the problem beyond straightforward analysis. We have omitted physical effects which affect this symmetry such as gravity, and as a consequence, we have confined our interest to processes which are followed for a short time or which have large spherically symmetric accelerations.

As we have already mentioned there are features of the nuclei in ordinary liquids which should be clarified. Among these is the distribution function for the number of nuclei in a liquid as a function of their effective size. Information of this kind has technological interest in boiling heat transfer and in the behavior of water moderated nuclear reactors under power surges.

REFERENCES

1 Lord Rayleigh, *Phil. Mag.*, 34 (1917) 94.
2 P. S. Epstein and M. S. Plesset, *J. Chem. Phys.*, 18 (1950) 1505.
3 M. S. Plesset, *J. Appl. Mech.*, 20 (1949) 277.
4 W. E. Mathews, *Thesis*, Calif. Inst. of Tech., 1953.
5 F. R. Gilmore, *Calif. Inst. of Tech. Rept. No. 26-4* (1952).
6 M. S. Plesset and S. A. Zwick, *J. Appl. Phys.*, 25 (1954) 493.

7 M. S. PLESSET AND D-Y. HSIEH, *Phys. Fluids*, 3 (1960) 882.

8 D-Y. HSIEH AND M. S. PLESSET, *J. Acoust. Soc. Am.*, 33 (1961) 206.

9 M. STRASBERG, *J. Acoust. Soc. Am.*, 33 (1961) 359.

10 G. I. TAYLOR, *Proc. Roy. Soc. (London)*, A 201 (1950) 192.

11 M. S. PLESSET, *J. Appl. Phys.*, 25 (1954) 96.

12 M. S. PLESSET AND T. P. MITCHELL, *Quart. Appl. Math.*, 13 (1956) 419.

Growth and Decay of
Gas Bubbles in Liquids*

JOSEPH B. KELLER

Courant Institute of Mathematical Sciences
New York University, New York 3, New York

I. INTRODUCTION

Whenever a gas and liquid are in contact, some gas gradually dissolves in the liquid, forming a liquid-gas solution. If equilibrium is established across a plane interface, the concentration c_0 of dissolved gas attains a value c_s, called the saturation concentration, which is proportional to the gas density ϱ. If $c_0 < c_s$ the solution is said to be undersaturated, while if $c_0 < c_s$ it is supersaturated. If there is a bubble in the liquid it may decay in size as the gas within it dissolves or grow in size if gas escapes from solution into the bubble. We would expect any bubble in an undersaturated solution to decay in size and disappear in a finite time, and we will prove that this is so. However in a supersaturated solution we shall see that because of surface tension, the behavior of a spherical bubble depends upon its initial radius R_0. For each concentration c_0 there is an equilibrium radius R_e such that for $R_0 = R_e$ the bubble remains in unstable equilibrium. For $R_0 < R_e$ it decays and disappears in a finite time while for $R_0 > R_e$ it grows indefinitely. If the solution is just saturated every bubble will decay unless surface tension is absent, in which case every bubble remains in neutral equilibrium. Although these results are physically obvious, we shall prove them mathematically from the appropriate physical laws. Our proofs, which do not depend upon solving the equations, may be of interest in other problems.

Bubbles may form spontaneously in a solution around a 'nucleus', which may be a solid particle, a hole in the liquid, an ion, etc. An undersaturated solution is obviously stable against bubble formation, since all bubbles will decay. The results above show that *a supersaturated solution is also stable* since all sufficiently small bubbles (those with $R_0 < R_e$) will dissolve. This result is in agreement with experience since supersaturated solutions, such as carbonated beverages, are of

* This research was supported by the National Science Foundation under Grant No. G19671. Reproduction in whole or in part is permitted for any purpose of the U.S. Government.

References p. 29

common occurrence, which would not be the case if they were unstable. Bubbles can grow only if they are produced with a radius greater than R_e. In a glassful of carbonated water, growing bubbles do occur, but they form only at the surface of the glass. Presumably only there do nuclei occur which can produce sufficiently large bubbles. These and some other considerations enable us to estimate the time required for an uncovered glassful of supersaturated carbonated water to get flat. We find that the dissolved gas concentration decays exponentially in time to the saturation concentration at a rate depending upon the number of nuclei on the surface, the volume of liquid and certain other constants.

In a closed container, in the absence of gravity, equilibrium may occur with a number of bubbles present. We find that all the bubbles must be of the same size and that if N bubbles are present, the mass m of gas in the container must exceed a critical value m_N, which increases with N. For each $m > m_N$ the pressure p_0 in the liquid and the common radius of the bubbles are uniquely determined. Other equilibria with any number of bubbles less than N are also possible, but the only stable equilibrium is that with just one bubble. In a closed container of carbonated water there is only one bubble, in agreement with this result, but it is above the liquid and its formation is largely due to gravity, which is not accounted for in the theory. Therefore this agreement is not very significant. However the Russian astronaut, Colonel Nikolayev, reported an observation of a closed bottle containing liquid and gas, which he made while orbiting around the earth in a satellite. The gas formed a single spherical bubble near the center of the bottle. Since the gravitational acceleration in an orbiting satellite is counterbalanced by the centrifugal acceleration, this observation provides confirmation of our result.

These results apply to homogeneous distributions of bubbles in infinitely extended liquids if the container denotes a portion of the fluid. When the container volume is unity, the condition $m > m_N$, which states that the mass of gas per unit volume exceeds m_N, is necessary for the existence of an equilibrium with N bubbles per unit volume. The equilibrium pressure depends upon the volume of gas and liquid, thus yielding an equation of state for the mixture of bubbles and solution.

In obtaining the result described above we have taken account of diffusion of dissolved gas toward or away from the bubble. We have also utilized the fact that at the bubble surface the concentration of dissolved gas is a constant fraction of the gas density in the bubble. Surface tension, which makes the pressure in the bubble higher than that in the liquid, has also been included. These same mechanisms were taken into account by EPSTEIN AND PLESSET[1] in their study of the rate of growth or shrinkage of a bubble, for which they obtained several approximate solutions. Convection of dissolved gas by the moving liquid has been taken into account in the study of vapor bubble growth and decay by PLESSET AND ZWICK[2] and by BIRKHOFF, MARGULIES AND HORNING[3].

References p. 29

Upon examining in detail the physical processes occurring at the bubble surface, we find that the macroscopic conservation laws do not suffice to determine the velocity of the surface. This is analogous to the indeterminacy in the theory of detonations. We conclude that it can be resolved by invoking the principle of the minimum rate of entropy production.

Finally we describe various bounds which can be obtained on the rates of growth and decay of bubbles by using physical considerations and special solutions.

In section 2 the problem of bubble growth or decay is formulated and the equilibrium solutions for a single bubble are obtained. In section 3 it is proved that bubbles grow or decay under appropriate conditions. Bubbles in closed containers are considered in section 4 and the escape of gas from a solution is treated in section 5. Section 6 contains a general discussion of phase transition processes and the principle of the minimum rate of entropy production. In section 7 bounds on the bubble growth and decay rates are described.

2. FORMULATION AND EQUILIBRIUM SOLUTIONS

Let $c(r, t)$ denote the concentration of dissolved gas in the liquid and let $R(t)$ be the radius of the bubble at time t. The concentration satisfies the diffusion equation

$$k^{-1}c_t = \nabla^2 c, \qquad r > R(t) \tag{2.1}$$

The constant k is the diffusivity of the gas in the liquid. We assume that initially the concentration has the constant value c_0 and the bubble radius is R_0. Thus

$$c(r, 0) = c_0, \qquad r > R_0 \tag{2.2}$$

$$R(0) = R_0 \tag{2.3}$$

At the bubble surface the concentration is proportional to the density of the gas in the bubble. The proportionality constant d is characteristic of the gas and liquid. Thus if $\varrho(t)$ denotes the (uniform) gas density in the bubble we have

$$c(R, t) = d\varrho(t) \tag{2.4}$$

The density ϱ is related to the bubble pressure p by the equation of state $\varrho = \varrho(p)$. This equation also involves the temperature (or entropy) of the gas, which we assume to be constant. The pressure p in the bubble exceeds the pressure p_0 in the liquid by the amount $2\sigma/R$ where σ is the surface tension of the interface. Thus the equation of state leads to

$$\varrho = \varrho \left(p_0 + \frac{2\sigma}{R} \right) \tag{2.5}$$

Finally, we must consider conservation of mass of the gas. This implies that the

References p. 29

rate of change of mass in the bubble equals the flux through the surface. The flux is $kc_r + \dot{R}c$ where the second term is due to convection. Thus we have

$$\left(\frac{4\pi}{3}R^3\varrho\right)^{\cdot} = 4\pi R^2\left[kc_r(R,t) + \dot{R}c(R,t)\right] \qquad (2.6)$$

Before examining these equations we first eliminate ϱ from (2.4) and (2.6) by using (2.5). We also eliminate $c(R,t)$ from (2.6) by means of (2.4). Then we obtain

$$c(R,t) = d\varrho\left(p_0 + \frac{2\sigma}{R}\right) \qquad (2.7)$$

$$\dot{R}\left\{[1 - d]\varrho\left(p_0 + \frac{2\sigma}{R}\right) - \frac{2\sigma}{3R}\varrho'\left(p_0 + \frac{2\sigma}{R}\right)\right\} = kc_r(R,t) \qquad (2.8)$$

The problem we consider is that of solving (2.1) — (2.3), (2.7) and (2.8) for $c(r,t)$ and $R(t)$.

An equilibrium solution is one in which R and c are both independent of t, so $R = R_0$, $c = c_0$. These values of R and c satisfy (2.1) — (2.3) and (2.8) while (2.7) becomes

$$c_0 = d\varrho\left(p_0 + \frac{2\sigma}{R_0}\right) \qquad (2.9)$$

This equation is not satisfied for any R_0 if the concentration c_0 is less than the saturation concentration $c_s = d\varrho(p_0)$, because ϱ is an increasing function of its argument. Thus there is no equilibrium solution with a bubble present in an undersaturated solution. On the other hand, if the solution is supersaturated $(c_0 > c_s)$ then (2.9) is satisfied for just one value of R_0 which we will call R_e, the equilibrium radius. From (2.9) it is given by

$$R_e = \frac{2\sigma}{p\left(\dfrac{c_0}{d}\right) - p_0} \qquad (2.10)$$

In the absence of surface tension $(\sigma = 0)$ (2.9) is satisfied for all R_0 if and only if the solution is saturated, *i.e.*, $c_0 = c_s$. For $\sigma \neq 0$ (2.9) cannot be satisfied by any R_0 when $c_0 = c_s$. Of course, for any value of c_0, equilibrium is possible without any bubble. All the above results also apply to equilibria with more than one bubble present, since all must have the same radius by (2.9).

3. GROWTH OR SHRINKAGE OF A BUBBLE

When the solution is unsaturated the only equilibrium configuration is that with no bubble present. We will show that in this case any bubble initially present

References p. 29

will gradually dissolve and finally disappear. However if the solution is super-saturated there are two equilibrium configurations: one with a bubble of radius R_e and another with no bubble. We will show that if a bubble is initially present with $R_0 < R_e$ it will dissolve and disappear, while if $R_0 > R_e$ the bubble will grow indefinitely.

To prove these statements, let us first consider the case $c_0 < d\varrho(p_0 + 2\sigma/R_0)$. This inequality is satisfied for all R_0 if $c_0 < c_s$ and for $R_0 < R_e$ if $c_0 \geq c_s$. The coefficient of $\dot{R}$ in (2.8) will be assumed to be positive for all R. This is true for an ideal gas if $d < \frac{2}{3}$. We wish to prove that $\dot{R} < 0$. Now initially the value of c at R_0 exceeds c_0 so that c is not continuous at the point $R = R_0$, $t = 0$. From this it may easily be shown that $\dot{R} < 0$ initially. We shall use this fact but omit its proof. Let us suppose that at some time $T > 0$, $\dot{R}(T)$ becomes zero for the first time. We will show that this is impossible, from which it will follow that $\dot{R} < 0$ for all t.

From (2.7) it follows that $c(R, t)$ increases as R decreases. Therefore $c(R, T) > c(R,t)$ for $T > t \geq 0$. Now by the well known maximum principle for parabolic equations, the maximum value of $c(r, t)$ for $0 \leq t \leq T$, $R(t) \leq r \leq R_1$ occurs at $t = 0$ or at $r = R(t)$ or at $r = R_1$. Here R_1 is an arbitrary constant. If we choose R_1 large enough then $c(R_1, t)$ is arbitrarily close to c_0, as can easily be shown. Since initially $c(R_0, 0) > c_0$ it therefore follows that the maximum of c cannot occur on the line $r = R_1$ nor on the line segment $t = 0$, $R_0 < r \leq R_1$. Thus the maximum of c must occur on the bubble surface $r = R(t)$. But we have seen that on this surface the maximum value is attained at $t = T$. Therefore $c(r, t)$ attains its maximum in the region $0 \leq t \leq T$, $R(t) \leq r \leq R_1$ at $t = T$, $r = R(T)$.

According to an unpublished lemma of NIRENBERG, based upon his strong maximum principle[4], it follows that c_r is strictly negative at the maximum of c. Thus we have $c_r[R(T), T] < 0$. But then from (2.8) it follows that $\dot{R}(T) < 0$. This contradicts the assumption that $\dot{R}(T) = 0$ which is therefore impossible. Thus it follows that $\dot{R} < 0$ for all t. Furthermore R cannot tend to a constant value other than zero, for this constant value would have to be an equilibrium radius and there is none smaller than R_0. In a similar way one can show that if $c_0 > c_s$ and $R_0 > R_e$ then the radius will increase indefinitely. This completes the proof of the statements in the first paragraph of this section.

4. BUBBLES IN A CLOSED CONTAINER

Suppose a closed container of volume V in the absence of gravity contains a volume V_L of liquid and a mass m of gas. Some of the gas may be dissolved in the liquid and the remainder will be contained in a number of bubbles, say N. Let us examine the equilibrium configurations of such a system. By (2.7) which must hold at each bubble, we see that since $c = c_0$ is constant, all the bubbles must have the same radius R. This radius is then determined by the condition that the bubbles fill the rest of the container, *i.e.* the part not containing liquid:

$$N \frac{4\pi}{3} R^3 = V - V_L \tag{4.1}$$

In order to determine the pressure p_0 in the liquid we consider the mass equation

$$m = \varrho \left(p_0 + \frac{2\sigma}{R} \right) [V + (d - 1)V_L] \tag{4.2}$$

This equation has a unique solution p_0 for each m provided that m is large enough. The right side of (4.2) increases monotonically with p_0 from its value at $p_0 = 0$, so we must have

$$m > \varrho \left(\frac{2\sigma}{R} \right) [V + (d - 1)V_L] = m_N \tag{4.3}$$

The right side of (4.3) depends upon N since R, given by (4.1), does. Therefore we call it m_N, the least mass (actually greatest lower bound) for equilibrium with N bubbles. If (4.3) is satisfied we can solve (4.2) for p_0 by writing the equation of state in the form $p = p(\varrho)$. Then (4.2) yields

$$p_0 = p(m[V + (d - 1)V_L]^{-1}) - 2\sigma \left[\frac{4\pi N}{3(V - V_L)} \right]^{\frac{1}{3}} \tag{4.4}$$

Eqn. (4.4) is the equation of state of the gas-liquid system, since it relates p_0 and V. The pressure in each bubble is $p(m[V + (d - 1)V_L]^{-1})$. If $\sigma = 0$ then $m_N = 0$ for all N, so equilibrium with any number of bubbles is possible for any $m > 0$.

From (4.1), R decreases as N increases, so from (4.3) m_N increases with N. Therefore if (4.3) is satisfied for some N, it is also satisfied for any $N' < N$. Thus if equilibrium with N bubbles is possible, equilibrium with any smaller number of bubbles is also possible. If $m < m_1$ equilibrium is impossible with any number of spherical bubbles. In this case the undissolved gas must assume a non-spherical shape which is possible only if it remains in contact with the container.

Since there are N different equilibria possible when $m_{N+1} > m > m_N$, it is important to consider their stability. First consider an equilibrium with more than one bubble present. Now if one bubble becomes smaller than equilibrium size, some other bubble may be larger. Consequently the small bubble will begin to decay (and disappear) while the larger one will grow. Therefore every equilibrium with more than one bubble present seems to be unstable. In the case of a

References p. 29

single bubble the size is fixed by the container and therefore no departure from equilibrium size is possible. Thus the only stable equilibrium is that with one bubble present. According to (4.4) this is also the equilibrium in which the liquid pressure p_0 is greatest.

5. ESCAPE OF GAS FROM SOLUTIONS

Let us consider a container holding a volume V of liquid in which gas is dissolved with initial concentration c_0. Suppose that the area of the container surface in contact with the liquid is S. If there are n nuclei per unit area of this surface then the total number of nuclei is nS. Suppose that on each nucleus a bubble grows until it reaches a size at which the buoyant force exerted on it by the liquid suffices to pull it off the surface. For a hemispherical bubble on the bottom the radius at breakaway is obtained by equating the buoyant force

$$\frac{1}{2} \cdot \frac{4\pi}{3} R^3 \varrho_1 g$$

to the surface tension force $2\pi R \sigma$ which holds the bubble to the surface. Here ϱ_1 is the liquid density and g is the acceleration of gravity. Upon equating these forces we find that $R = (3\sigma/\varrho_1 g)^{\frac{1}{2}}$.

The time t_0 required for a bubble to grow from radius R_0 to radius R can be determined from the quasi-static solution for R as a function of time. This solution is approximately[1]

$$R^2 = R_0{}^2 + 2(c - c_s)k\varrho^{-1}t_0 \tag{5.1}$$

In this equation c denotes the concentration far from the bubble, assumed to be constant during its growth. If we neglect $R_0{}^2$ then (5.1) yields for t_0 the result

$$t_0 = \frac{\varrho R^2}{2k(c - c_s)} \tag{5.2}$$

Now the mass of dissolved gas in excess of the saturation value is $(c - c_s)V$ where $c = c(t)$ is the concentration. The rate of loss of the gas due to the growth and escape of the bubbles considered above is equal to the number of nuclei multiplied by the mass of gas per bubble divided by the time required for a bubble to grow to escape size. Thus we have the equation

$$\frac{d(c - c_s)V}{dt} = - nS \cdot \frac{1}{2} \cdot \frac{4\pi}{3} R^3 \varrho \cdot \frac{1}{t_0}$$
$$= - [4\pi nSk(\sigma/3\varrho_1 g)^{\frac{1}{2}}] (c - c_s) \tag{5.3}$$

The solution of this equation is

References p. 29

$$c(t) - c_s = (c_0 - c_s)e^{-t/\tau} \tag{5.4}$$

The decay constant τ is

$$\tau = \frac{V}{4\pi knS}\left(\frac{3\varrho_1 g}{\sigma}\right)^{\frac{1}{2}} \tag{5.5}$$

Let us compare τ with the decay constant $\tau' = 4L^2/k\pi^2$ for loss of gas by diffusion through the top surface of the liquid, where L is the depth of liquid. If we apply (5.5) to a cube of liquid of edge L with a free top surface then $V = L^3$ and $S = 5L^2$ so $V/S = L/5$. In this case we have

$$\frac{\tau}{\tau'} = \frac{\pi}{80nL}\left(\frac{3\varrho_1 g}{\sigma}\right)^{\frac{1}{2}} = \frac{0.24}{nL} \tag{5.6}$$

In (5.6) we have set $\varrho_1 = 1$ gm/cm^3, $g = 980$ cm/sec^2 and $\sigma = 80$ dyn/cm which is appropriate for water. Then if n exceeds $1/10$ nucleation site/cm^2 and L exceeds 10 cm, we see that $\tau' > 4\tau$ so gas loss by bubble formation is more important than loss by diffusion through the surface. From (5.5) we see that the method of producing the solution has no effect on the rate of escape of gas. Therefore, no particular method of especial carbonation of beverages provides any longer life for the solution than any other method yielding the same dissolved gas concentration. Polishing the inner surface of the glass might be effective in keeping the gas from escaping if it reduced the number of nuclei.

6. GENERAL CONSIDERATIONS AND THE MINIMUM RATE OF ENTROPY PRODUCTION

The growth or decay of a bubble is a phase transition process in which matter goes from the solution phase into the gas phase or vice versa. Other phase transition processes are the freezing of a liquid, the evaporation of a liquid, the transition of a conductor from the normal state to the superconducting state, the detonation of an explosive gas mixture, the tarnishing reaction in steel, etc. These processes have many features in common, which permit results concerning any one of them to be applied to some of the others. One such feature is that they have not been successfully analyzed from the viewpoint of the atomic theory of matter. Not only is a kinetic theory of them lacking, but even an equilibrium theory based upon statistical mechanics is undeveloped. Consequently they are analyzed on the basis of a macroscopic or continuum theory of matter, such as we have used here.

In the continuum theory the transition between phases is assumed to occur across an infinitely thin layer which is represented as a surface of discontinuity. The motion of this surface must be determined in the course of analyzing the process, so such an analysis leads to a free boundary problem. Mathematically such

References p. 29

a problem is one in which one must determine part of the boundary of a region while simultaneously solving some equations within the region, boundary conditions being given on the unknown boundary. Among the boundary conditions to be satisfied at a phase transition surface are the conditions following from conservation of mass, momentum and energy across the surface. The discontinuity in internal energy across such a surface is called the latent heat of transition (*e.g.* latent heat of fusion, of evaporation, of solution). We have ignored it in the foregoing analysis and will comment on its consequences below.

We have found that the conservation laws just mentioned and the properties of the matter on one side of a phase transition surface do not suffice to uniquely determine the velocity of the surface. Even the additional requirement that the entropy must increase as matter crosses the surface does not lead to a single velocity. This difficulty is well known in the theory of detonations and is resolved there by the postulation of an additional condition, called the Chapman-Jouget condition, the consequences of which usually agree with experiment. We propose that an additional condition should be imposed in all phase transitions, namely that entropy should be produced at the minimum rate compatible with the other conditions. This is a principle which has become accepted in irreversible thermo-dynamics. In the case of detonations, it leads to the Chapman-Jouget condition, which suggests that it is correct. The need for the above condition has usually been avoided by specifying the temperature at which transition occurs, or by specifying the latent heat as a function of the transition temperature, or by imposing some similar condition.

In the bubble growth or decay problem as well as in that of the growth or decay of a liquid drop by condensation, the concentration of diffusing gas obeys the diffusion equation. In melting, freezing and vapor bubble problems, on the other hand, only heat is assumed to flow and the temperature also satisfies the diffusion or heat equation. Consequently when surface tension is omitted, the gas bubble problem becomes formally identical with problems of melting, freezing, liquid drops and vapor bubbles. In problems of transition of a superconductor to the normal state due to a supercritical magnetic field, the magnetic field also satisfies the diffusion equation[5]. One and two dimensional problems involving such transitions are also formally identical with problems involving the transitions just mentioned. When latent heat is taken into account in the gas bubble, liquid drop and super-normal transition problems, heat flow must be considered and the heat equation for the temperature must be solved. In these cases both the diffusion equation for gas or magnetic field and the heat equation for temperature must be solved simultaneously. They are coupled through the conditions imposed at the transition surface. Thus these problems are more complicated than those which just involve heat flow.

References p. 29

7. GROWTH AND DECAY RATES

A number of conclusions about the rate of growth or decay of a bubble can be arrived at by physical intuition. For example we would expect a growing bubble to grow faster and a decaying bubble to decay slower (*i.e.*, to have a larger radius $R(t)$ at any time $t > 0$) if the initial concentration c_0 is increased, if the surface tension σ is decreased, if the initial radius R_0 is increased, if the proportionality constant d in (2.4) is decreased or if the pressure p_0 in the liquid is decreased. These conclusions may be summarized by saying that for $t > 0$, $R(t)$ should increase if R_0/R_e is increased, where R_e is the equilibrium radius given by (2.10). On the other hand, if the diffusivity k is increased a growing bubble should grow faster while a decaying one should decay faster. Furthermore when $\sigma = 0$ a spherical bubble should grow or decay faster than a circular cylindrical bubble of the same initial radius which in turn should grow or decay faster than a slab of gas of initial width $2R_0$. These latter conclusions follow from the fact that the sphere has a larger ratio of surface area to volume than a cylinder, which has a larger ratio than a slab. The conclusion for a decaying bubble remains valid when $\sigma > 0$, since surface tension increases the pressure twice as much in a spherical bubble than in a cylindrical one of the same radius, and not at all in a slab bubble.

The preceding conclusions can be used to obtain bounds on the radius $R(t)$ and on the disappearance time t_0, defined by $R(t_0) = 0$. For example let us consider a decaying bubble. Its diameter $2R(t)$ is smaller at any time $t > 0$ than the width $2x(t)$ of a slab of initial width $2x(0) = 2R_0$. In studying the growth or decay of a slab, it is clear that the two surfaces of the slab move independently of each other since there is no motion of the gas within the slab. In fact each surface moves as if the gas region were of semi-infinite extent. But the problem of the semi-infinite gas region contains no intrinsic length since σ does not occur in it. It is identical with that of the freezing of a lake, which was solved by STEPHAN[6] in 1889. Dimensional analysis implies that $x(t) - x(0) = -b\sqrt{kt}$ and

$$c = c_0 f\left(\frac{x - x_0}{\sqrt{kt}}\right)$$

where b is a dimensionless constant and f a dimensionless function. It is possible to find f explicitly in terms of b and to obtain a transcendental equation for the determination of b. Then for $t > 0$, $R(t) < R_0 - b\sqrt{kt}$ and $t_0 < R_0^2/kb^2$. This bound incidentally shows that the bubble disappears in a finite time. For a growing bubble with $\sigma = 0$ (*i.e.*, surface tension negligible), the same considerations yield $R(t) > R_0 + b_1\sqrt{kt}$ where b_1 is a different dimensionless constant. One conclusion from this bound is that the bubble grows indefinitely.

References p. 29

When $\sigma = 0$ another bound on the radius of a growing bubble can be obtained by comparing it with a bubble which starts from a point (*i.e.*, $R_0 = 0$). In this case a similarity solution is also possible and yields $R(t) = b_2\sqrt{kt}$. It was first obtained by ZENER[7] who was studying the growth of particles in a solid solution. Thus for a growing bubble with initial radius $R_0 > 0$, we have $R(t) > b_2\sqrt{kt}$. A similarity solution yielding $R(t) = b_3\sqrt{kt}$ for a bubble starting from a point can also be obtained when convection is taken into account. It has been obtained for vapor bubbles by BIRKHOFF, MARGULIES AND HORNING[3]. We have also found such solutions when heat flow, convection and diffusion are all taken into account. They can be found for slabs, cylindrical bubbles and spherical bubbles. These solutions can also be used to provide bounds on the radii of bubbles with finite initial radius. In addition there are similarity solutions even when the diffusivity depends upon concentration, as has been shown by MIRANKER AND KELLER[8].

Bounds on $R(t)$ can also be obtained from the approximate solution derived by the so-called quasi-static method[1, 5]. In this method one omits the term c_t in the diffusion equation (2.1) and replaces the initial condition

$$c(r, t) = c_0 \text{ by } \lim_{r \to \infty} c(r, t) = c_0.$$

Then $c(r, t) = c_0 + A(t)r^{-1}$. The function $A(t)$ and the radius $R(t)$ can be found from the two boundary conditions (2.7) and (2.8). This approximate solution can be shown to be greater than the actual solution for a decaying bubble and smaller than it for a growing bubble. The proof is similar to that which we have given for the super-normal transition of a superconductor[5].

REFERENCES

1 P. S. EPSTEIN AND M. S. PLESSET, *J. Chem. Phys.*, 18 (1950) 1505–9.
2 M. S. PLESSET AND S. A. ZWICK, *J. Appl. Phys.*, 23 (1952) 95–98; 25 (1954) 493–500; *J. Math. and Phys.*, 33 (1955) 308–330.
3 G. BIRKHOFF, R. S. MARGULIES AND W. A. HORNING, *Phys. Fluids*, 1 (1958) 201–204.
4 L. NIRENBERG, *Comm. Pure Appl. Math.*, VI (1953) 167–177.
5 J. B. KELLER, *Phys. Rev.*, 111 (1958) 1497–1499.
6 J. STEFAN, *S. B. Kais. Akad. Wiss. Wien*, 98 (1889) 473.
7 C. ZENER, *J. Appl. Phys.* 20 (1949) 950.
8 W. L. MIRANKER AND J. B. KELLER, *J. Math. Mech.*, 9 (1960) 67–70.

Flow around a Bubble
Rising in a Tube

P. R. GARABEDIAN

Institute of Mathematical Sciences,
New York University, New York, New York

Consider a half-space of water situated above a mass of air whose pressure just balances the weight of the water. The equilibrium of such a configuration is evidently unstable, for the force of gravity will immediately cause the water to start dripping down into the air. This is an elementary example of the *Taylor instability* that may occur at the interface between two fluids of unequal densities.

Experience shows that the air tends to penetrate the water in a series of elongated bubbles which rise at a fairly steady rate. This has led Taylor to study the steady motion of a single bubble rising in a vertical tube of liquid. It is our aim here to discuss the potential flow past such a bubble. The existence of the flow can be demonstrated by filling a glass tube with stained water, being sure to leave a little extra space for air, then corking up the tube and tipping it over quickly to allow the bubble of air to rise from the bottom to the top.

To be more precise, we shall investigate plane flow governed by a complex potential $\zeta = \phi + i\psi$ that is an analytic function of the complex variable $z = x + iy$. We shall suppose that the flow is directed downwards through a vertical strip $-l/2 < x < l/2$ and past an infinitely long bubble of fixed shape. Along the walls $x = \pm l/2$ of the strip the stream function ψ takes on constant boundary values $\psi = \pm Ul/2$, where U represents the speed of the liquid at the upper end $y = +\infty$ of the tube. Assuming that the bubble is shaped symmetrically with respect to the y-axis, we find, on the other hand, that we must have $\psi = 0$ on the free streamline bounding the bubble.

Bernoulli's law asserts that

$$\tfrac{1}{2}q^2 + \frac{p}{\varrho} + gy = \text{const.} ,$$

where q, p and ϱ stand for the speed, pressure and density of the liquid, and where g is the acceleration of gravity. Since the inertia of air is negligible compared with that of water, we may put $p = 0$ throughout the bubble. The requirement that

References p. 33

the pressure p remain continuous across the interface between the air and the water now yields the *free boundary condition*

$$\tfrac{1}{2}q^2 + gy = 0$$

there, provided that we place the origin of coordinates at the same height as the apex of the bubble, where $q = 0$. The free boundary condition may be thought of as determining the shape of the free streamline at the interface between the water and the air, which is not given in advance.

It is of interest in the applications to estimate the speed at which Taylor bubbles penetrate a liquid. Therefore what we need to know is the *Froude number* $U/\sqrt{gl}$ of the flow just described. However, attempts of BIRKHOFF AND CARTER[1,2] and of the author[3] to evaluate the Froude number have led to the conclusion that the flow itself is not uniquely determined. In fact, it turns out that there is a one-parameter family of essentially different stream functions ψ satisfying the boundary value problem we have formulated. Our task thus becomes to single out the one representing the actual flow that is observed.

On physical grounds it may be argued that from any family of flows representing the motion of a bubble in a tube, the only one which could be stable would be that corresponding to the most rapid climb of the bubble. Our contention is that a bubble of any other form would tend to change its shape so as to rise faster and consequently lose potential energy more quickly. These considerations lead us to an extremal problem that characterizes the physically realistic motion of the bubble in a unique way.

Let ψ stand for a stream function defining the flow past a tentative bubble shape bounded by an admissible trial curve C. In general $q^2/(-2y)$ will not be constant on C, which is not assumed to be a constant pressure free streamline. However, we may introduce a functional g of C given by the formula

$$g(C) = \max_{C} \frac{q^2}{(-2y)}.$$

Our assertion is that the free streamline of the unique stable flow past a bubble within the strip $-l/2 < x < l/2$ is a curve C solving the extremal problem

$$g(C) = \text{minimum}.$$

The above minimax characterization of a Taylor bubble becomes easier to justify physically after it has been formulated somewhat differently. Application of an appropriate change of scale to ψ shows that the following extremal problem is equivalent: Let the numbers l and g be fixed, and restrict the shape of C so that all along it the inequality

$$\frac{q^2}{(-2y)} \leqq g$$

holds. Subject to these constraints, the stable free streamline is found to be the curve C for which

$$U = U(C) = \text{maximum.}$$

It is clear that both formulations of our extremal problem amount to choosing the curve C so that the dimensionless Froude number $U/\sqrt{gl}$ becomes a maximum. This remark suggests procedures for calculating rigorous lower bounds on the Froude number. Indeed, if we compute the functional $g(C)$ for any reasonable guess C of the true free streamline, then the number $U/\sqrt{g(C)l}$ represents such a lower bound. What remains is to pick C systematically from a family of curves developed through analysis of the free boundary condition.

Let us renormalize so that $Ul/2 = 1$, and so that $x = \psi = 0$ along one of the walls of our tube. If we extend the flow across that wall by means of the Schwarz principle of reflection, we obtain a freely falling jet of liquid in some neighborhood of $y = -\infty$. It is our intention to derive a difference-differential equation satisfied there by the complex potential ζ.

The free boundary condition may be rewritten in the form

$$\frac{d\zeta}{dz}\frac{d\bar{\zeta}}{d\bar{z}} + g\,\frac{z - \bar{z}}{i} = 0,$$

which is equivalent to

$$\frac{i}{g} + (z - \bar{z})\,\frac{dz}{d\phi}\frac{d\bar{z}}{d\phi} = 0.$$

On the other hand, because the reflected image with respect to the y-axis of any point z on the free boundary of our jet is another such point corresponding to the complex number $-\bar{z}$, we have

$$z(\phi - i) = - \overline{z(\phi + i)}$$

for all sufficiently large and negative values of ϕ. Putting this result into the free boundary condition we establish the desired difference-differential equation

$$z'(\phi + i)z'(\phi - i)\,[z(\phi + i) + z(\phi - i)] = i/g,$$

which also remains valid when ϕ is replaced by ζ.

Asymptotic solutions of the above difference-differential equation have been

References p. 33

used to define reasonable trial curves C for the estimation of the Froude number associated with Taylor's bubble. In this way it has been shown that

$$\frac{U}{\sqrt{gl}} \geqq 0.23 \; .$$

It would be desirable to find similar approximations to the Froude number of an axially symmetric bubble rising in a cylindrical tube.

REFERENCES

1 G. BIRKHOFF AND D. CARTER, *Rept. LA–1927*, Los Alamos Scientific Laboratory, 1956.
2 G. BIRKHOFF AND D. CARTER, Rising Plane Bubbles, *J. Math. Mech.*, 6 (1957) 769.
3 P. R. GARABEDIAN, On Steady-State Bubbles Generated by Taylor Instability, *Proc. Roy. Soc. (London)*, A241 (1957) 423.

Measurements of Bubble Growth During Mass Transfer

J. W. WESTWATER

*Department of Chemistry and Chemical Engineering
University of Illinois, Urbana, Illinois*

ABSTRACT

Bubbles can grow in liquids under conditions such that the diffusion of mass is part of the process controlling the rate of growth. The present state of knowledge is discussed in this writing. Illustrative data are given for the growth of bubbles during electrolysis, growth of bubbles when the ambient pressure is decreased on a liquid containing dissolved gas, and growth of bubbles in a boiling, binary-liquid mixture. The principal weaknesses in our present knowledge concern the wall effect; the effects of viscosity, surface tension, and inertia; the uncertainties due to natural variability; and the interference between neighboring bubbles. These are discussed in the following.

INTRODUCTION

Cavitation means the creation and growth of a hole in a liquid. At times it is a very desirable occurrence, such as in the reboiler of a distillation unit. At other times it is quite undesirable, around a ship's screw for example. In either case, knowledge about the creation of cavities is valuable. The growth problem is of special interest when one intends deliberately to utilize cavitation.

The birth of cavities, that is nucleation, will receive minimum attention in this writing. Rather, stress will be given to the phenomenon of cavity growth. The inverse problem, cavity collapse, will be introduced indirectly only. Although cavities may have very irregular shapes, this writing will be concerned only with those which are more or less spherical and which may be called bubbles.

THREE CONTROLLING MECHANISMS

What controls the rate of growth of a bubble? A bubble will grow as fast as it can, with its rate being retarded by some natural process or processes. Three regulatory mechanisms are evident.

Mechanical forces can control the rate of growth. RAYLEIGH[1] showed this in 1917. He considered the case of an empty bubble (a perfect vacuum inside) in the midst of a pool of non-volatile, inviscid, incompressible liquid of zero surface tension. He set up the force balance consisting of the force of the ambient atmosphere on the liquid pool and the resulting acceleration of all the liquid as it moved toward the center of the bubble. The result was the familar Rayleigh equation for bubble collapse. All heat effects were neglected, and mass diffusion was assumed zero.

A second case was also solved by Rayleigh. This treated a compressible, but insoluble, gas inside the bubble and considered the force exerted by this.

Subsequent writers improved the force balance to incorporate forces due to viscosity, surface tension, and vapor pressure. The so-called extended Rayleigh equation, in a form modified from SCRIVEN[2] is shown as eqn. (1).

$$R \frac{d^2R}{d\theta^2} + \left(2 - \frac{\varepsilon}{2}\right) \left(\frac{dR}{d\theta}\right)^2 + \frac{2\sigma}{\varepsilon \varrho_L R} + \frac{4\mu_L}{\varrho_L R}\left(\frac{dR}{d\theta}\right) = \frac{P_v + P_i - P_\infty}{\varepsilon \varrho_L} \quad (1)$$

(Force Balance)

It implies a spherical bubble. External body forces are not included in the equation, although they may at times be significant (for example in a strong electric field). Forces due to surface-dilational viscosity have likewise been omitted here, although introduced at a later date[3].

Suppose a growing bubble is completely controlled by mechanical forces. Then to discover how the radius R depends on time θ, one must select the proper boundary conditions and integrate eqn. (1), the force balance (also known as the equation of motion). Although no one has succeeded in doing this without significant simplification, eqn. (1) is nevertheless informative and of real use. For example consider the simplified case of a collapsing cavity as solved by Rayleigh (no surface tension, no viscosity, but with inert gas present). For this case a very high pressure is predicted before the inward rush of the liquid is spent. A slightly different case, a vacuum-hole, is predicted to give rise to large pressure shocks upon collapse. Experience verifies these predictions. The fact that mechanical damage to solid surfaces can result from these pressures is well known. Apparently mechanical forces do control the rate of growth or collapse for some bubbles.

The transfer of heat is a second mechanism that can control the rate of growth or collapse of a bubble. Consider a one-component system consisting of a bubble of saturated vapor suspended in its liquid. If the liquid is superheated, the bubble will grow; whereas if the liquid is subcooled, the bubble will shrink. All phase changes, in reality, are accompanied by a latent heat of phase change. Thus a growing vapor bubble must be supplied with heat. The energy will be conducted from the hottest parts of the liquid, far from the bubble, up to the bubble wall.

Heat transfer of course is a rate process which is governed by familiar factors such as a temperature driving force, thermal conductivity, and fluid convection.

If we choose the simple case of spherical symmetry and assume that the vapor bubble and its liquid are both incompressible, eqn. (2) is obtained.

$$\frac{Q}{\varrho_L C_L} + \alpha_L \left[\frac{\partial^2 T}{\partial r^2} + \frac{2}{r} \frac{\partial T}{\partial r} \right] = \frac{\partial T}{\partial \theta} + \frac{\varepsilon R^2}{r^2} \cdot \frac{dR}{d\theta} \cdot \frac{\partial T}{\partial r} \tag{2}$$

(Heat Balance)

This is a heat balance for a thin spherical shell of liquid surrounding the bubble. It includes heat conduction in and out, heat transport by radial flow of the liquid, possible heat generation, and sensible heat storage and depletion.

Strictly speaking, during phase change eqn. (2) must always be considered simultaneously with eqn. (1). Put another way, if a bubble growth can be described accurately by eqn. (2), then it can also be described accurately by eqn. (1). If all boundary conditions were known exactly, one could use either equation to find R vs. θ. In practice, all boundary conditions are never known exactly. However, in certain cases it is possible to show that one can make a much better estimate of the boundary conditions for the heat balance than for the force balance. In these cases we say that heat transfer is the controlling mechanism. As an example, when actual bubble growth data, for boiling pure components, such as are now available from several sources[4, 5, 6] are substituted in the left side of eqn. (1), one finds that $P_v + P_i - P_\infty$ is very small. An accurate value of this ΔP term would be needed if one wishes to go backwards—that is integrate eqn. (1) to predict R vs. θ. It seems very unlikely that we will have, a priori, good values for this pressure term. However, one can use eqn. (2) in this case with much better accuracy. The fact that ΔP is nil means that the bubble vapor practically is at its saturation temperature, and thus a necessary boundary condition is established with satisfactory accuracy.

Even if heat transfer is controlling, some simplifications are adopted by all writers before eqn. (2) is integrated. For example, PLESSET AND ZWICK[7], FORSTER AND ZUBER[8], SCRIVEN[2], and BIRKHOFF, MARGULIES, AND HORNING[9] all assume perfect radial symmetry, no heat generation, perfect mixing inside the bubble, an infinite body of liquid, and no forced convection.

A third mechanism that can control the rate of growth or collapse of a bubble is mass diffusion. If a gas bubble is suspended in a liquid solvent, the bubble will grow or shrink, depending on whether the concentration of dissolved gas in the liquid is high or low. Consider bubble growth. Solute molecules must diffuse

References p. 53–54

through the liquid, from far away, up to the bubble wall. The bubble can grow no faster than it receives the supply of solute molecules.

If we choose the simple case of spherical symmetry and assume that the gas and liquid phases have constant densities, eqn. (3) is obtained.

$$D \left[\frac{\partial^2 C}{\partial r^2} + \frac{2}{r} \frac{\partial C}{\partial r} \right] = \frac{\partial C}{\partial \theta} + \frac{\varepsilon R^2}{r^2} \cdot \frac{dR}{d\theta} \cdot \frac{\partial C}{\partial r} \tag{3}$$

(Mass Balance on Solute)

This is a mass balance on the solute, for a thin spherical shell of liquid surrounding the bubble. It includes mass diffusion in and out, mass transport by radial flow of the liquid, and mass storage or depletion. Generation and depletion of mass by chemical reactions are assumed non-existent. The system is assumed to consist of two components only.

To be precise, eqn. (3) must always be considered simultaneously with eqns. (1) and (2). If all boundary conditions were known exactly, one could use any of the three equations to predict R vs. θ during bubble growth accompanied by mass transfer. However, in some cases good estimates of the boundary conditions for eqn. (3) can be made, whereas the estimates for eqns. (1) and (2) are in grave doubt. In such cases interest centers on eqn. (3), and we say that mass transfer is controlling. The solution of air bubbles in water is a good example. The growth of gas bubbles during electrolysis is another.

A particularly complicated situation arises if both heat and mass transfer are controlling. Put another way, we may have no confidence that our estimates of the boundary conditions for eqn. (3) are any better than the estimates for eqn. (2). This situation occurs during bubble growth in boiling binary liquid mixtures. The procedure then is to retain both eqns. (2) and (3), combining them to solve for a troublesome boundary condition. The troublesome factor so selected is the condition of the bubble, that is, its temperature and composition.

SCRIVEN[2] has carried out the formidable task of simultaneously solving eqns. (2) and (3). He used numerical techniques on a digital computer and made simplifying assumptions such as: bubble radius proportional to square root of time, uniform initial concentration, uniform initial superheat, vapor-liquid equilibrium always in existence at the bubble wall, perfect radial symmetry, and physical properties independent of temperature. Two specific systems were solved for: glycol-water and glycerol-water.

GAS EVOLUTION DURING ELECTROLYSIS

Gas bubbles are frequently formed during electrolysis. The bubbles appear at specific active sites on the electrodes. Microscopic examination of these sites[10, 11] show that they are pits and scratches. The fact that pits and scratches of the right sizes and shapes should be effective gas traps has been shown theoretically by BANKOFF[12]. Apparently one requirement for a heterogeneous nucleation site to be active for a liquid-to-gas phase change is that the site contain some trapped gas.

The electrolysis process may be visualized by considering as an example the evolution of hydrogen from water. Hydrogen ions migrate through the water in response to the electric field in the liquid. At the cathode the ions receive electrons and become molecules or atoms of hydrogen in solution. These dissolved molecules diffuse throughout the liquid and soon result in a supersaturated liquid. The amount of supersaturation depends on conditions, but for laboratory tests with hydrogen production from acids and bases it can vary from about 3 to 30 times the equilibrium concentration. Eventually a bubble starts to grow at a nucleation site. Liquid at the bubble wall soon loses its extra dissolved hydrogen and becomes saturated or nearly so. New hydrogen is supplied to the bubble wall by diffusion from the supersaturated liquid farther away. The bubble growth rate is fixed by the rate of transport of dissolved hydrogen through the liquid.

Eqn. (3) is the logical expression to use for this situation. SCRIVEN[2] integrated the equation by numerical means. He assumed that the form of the correct solution is eqn. (4).

$$R = 2\beta\sqrt{D\theta} \tag{4}$$

The dimensionless coefficient β is related to two dimensionless groups; one is ε (the density factor used also in eqns. (1), (2) and (3)), and one is a driving-force factor Φ. These are defined in eqns. (5) and (6).

$$\varepsilon = \frac{\varrho_L - \varrho_v}{\varrho_L} \tag{5}$$

$$\Phi = \left(\frac{\varrho_L}{\varrho_v}\right)\left(\frac{C_\infty - C_{sat}}{\varrho_L - C_{sat}}\right) \tag{6}$$

The numerical relationship of β, ε, and Φ is shown in Fig. 1. Perfect radial symmetry is assumed. At time zero the bubble is assumed to be of very small, finite size having zero velocity for the bubble wall.

Earlier workers made bold assumptions in order to obtain a solution to eqn. (3) in closed form. For example EPSTEIN AND PLESSET[13] assumed that mass transfer by radial flow of the liquid is negligible, and therefore the last term of eqn. (3) may be dropped. Eqn. (7) for the bubble wall velocity is the result.

$$\frac{dR}{d\theta} = \frac{D(C_\infty - C_{sat})}{\varrho_v} \left[\frac{1}{R} + \frac{1}{\sqrt{\pi D \theta}} \right] \qquad (7)$$

(Epstein-Plesset)

DOREMUS[14] presents an equation similar to eqn. (7) except that ϱ_v is replaced with $2 (\varrho_v - C_{sat})$, and the numerator 1 in the last term in the brackets is replaced with a dimensionless radius R_0/R. Doremus states that his equation is plausible for bubble collapse. Whether this is true for bubble growth is open to question.

Epstein and Plesset point out that an easy integration of eqn. (7) is possible

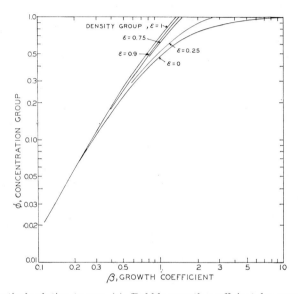

Fig. 1. Theoretical solution to eqn. (3). Bubble growth coefficient for mass transfer only.

when the term $1/\sqrt{\pi D \theta}$ may be neglected. The result is equivalent to eqn. (4) except that β is given now by eqn. (8) instead of by Fig. 1.

$$\beta = \left[\frac{C_\infty - C_{sat}}{2\varrho_v} \right]^{\frac{1}{2}}, \text{ approximate for small } \beta \qquad (8)$$

Neglect of the last term in eqn. (7) is logical for bubble collapse after enough time has elapsed. For collapse, R gets small as θ gets large, and the two terms in the brackets become different by orders of magnitude. However, during bubble growth, R and θ increase simultaneously. In fact, the two terms are of equal magnitude if $\beta = \frac{1}{2}\sqrt{\pi}$. What do experimental data for bubble growth indicate for the magnitude of β? This is discussed in the following sections.

References p. 53–54

Tests with Constant E.M.F.

Two publications contain data for bubble growth during electrolysis[10,15]. WES-
TERHEIDE AND WESTWATER[10] photographed hydrogen bubbles on a platinum
cathode using a constant voltage drop of about 1.5 volts across the cell. This gave
current densities between 0.03 and 0.21 A/cm². The data for bubble growth could
be represented fairly well by eqn. (4). Some of the data are shown in Fig. 2. The
supersaturations shown in the graph were not measured but were computed
from eqn. (4) and Fig. 1.

The experimental values of β were between 0.32 and 0.70. This order of magni-

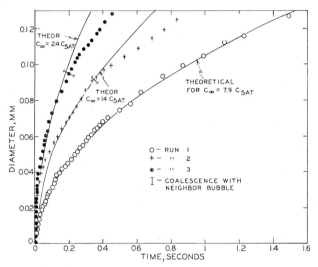

Fig. 2. Growth of hydrogen bubbles during electrolysis at constant E.M.F. Run 1: 1 N H₂SO₄,
1.24 volts; Run 2: 0.1 N H₂SO₄, 1.23 volts; Run 3: 0.1 N H₂SO₄, 1.47 volts.

tude is close to $\frac{1}{2}\sqrt{\pi}$, therefore for growing bubbles of hydrogen the use of eqn.
(8) is not justified.

The bubbles represented in Fig. 2 were isolated bubbles and had contact angles
of about 10 degrees. Fig. 3 illustrates one of these bubbles.

Admitting that the last term of eqn. (7) cannot be jettisoned, is eqn. (7) suitable
for describing the data in Fig. 2? Calculations show that the Epstein-Plesset
equation gives a growth rate which is low by 14% for Run 1 and low by 21%
for Run 3. Part of the 14 to 21% deviation arises because eqn. (7) does not include
mass transport by radial flow of the liquid. These deviations are not bad, so
transport of this kind is not highly important for hydrogen in dilute acid. But
radial convection transport can be much greater for other systems, and it is of
increasing importance with increasing growth rates.

Tests with Constant Current

GLAS AND WESTWATER[15] photographed bubbles of hydrogen and oxygen in acids and bases on platinum electrodes using a constant current rather than a constant E.M.F. for each run. The currents were between 0.013 and 0.133 A/cm^2.

The bubble growth rates again could be represented fairly well by eqn. (4), and values of β were computed from the R *vs.* θ data. At first thought, the agreement with eqn. (4) is surprising. On a macroscopic scale, the volumetric rate of

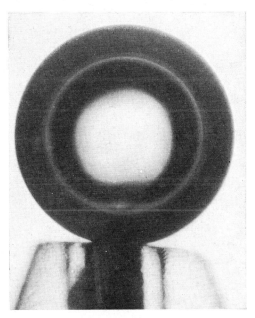

Fig. 3. Single hydrogen bubble with small contact angle. Liquid is dilute H_2SO_4 in water. Bubble diameter is 0.020 inch.

gas production must be constant when the electrical current is constant. However, the data show that what really happens on a microscopic scale is that any one bubble does grow with R approximately proportional to $\sqrt{\theta}$. The growth data do not give a good fit with a relation such as $R \propto \theta^{\frac{1}{3}}$. Conservation of mass requires, therefore, that the supersaturation in the liquid must vary during the growth of a single bubble. An alternate, but less likely, possibility is that the number of bubbles growing per unit area at any one time must vary in just the right manner to account for the constant current flow.

The choice of constant current or constant E.M.F. for bubbles formed during electrolysis is analogous to constant heat flux at the solid wall or constant hot-wall temperature for bubbles formed in boiling liquids. From the few published electrolysis tests we may predict for boiling that the form of the R vs. θ behavior for bubbles on a wall will be quite similar regardless of whether the flux or the ΔT happens to be the controlled variable. In both boiling cases we should expect that $R = 2\beta \sqrt{\alpha_L \theta}$ will be a fairly good description.

Mathematically, bubble growth by heat transfer only and by mass transfer only are analogous. A solution for either eqn. (2) or eqn. (3) can be converted to a solution for the other by an interchange of equivalent dimensionless groups; $D\theta/R^2$ is equivalent to $\alpha_L\theta/R^2$, and $(C_\infty - C_{sat})/\varrho_v$ is equivalent to $\varrho_L C_L \Delta T/(\varrho_v \lambda)$. Happily, this means that some factors for boiling liquids can be investigated by use of analogous electrolysis tests. Electrical quantities are frequently much easier to measure and control than are thermal quantities, so the experimental use of the analogy is very attractive.

DISSOLUTION OF GAS IN A LIQUID

When a bottle of soda-water is opened, many bubbles of carbon dioxide appear. The gas was present in solution at the original higher pressure. The heat of solution is very small, other heat effects are small, and the process of gas evolution is almost isothermal. Mass transfer may be argued to be the rate-controlling process that fixes the speed of growth of these bubbles.

Integration of eqn. (3) is the subject of several papers. As pointed out previously, SCRIVEN[2] solved the equation by numerical techniques and was able to retain the last term representing transport of mass by radial flow of the liquid. His solution is eqn. (4), with β being a constant exactly fixed by the liquid density, gas density, and the concentration driving force.

Experimental workers have given attention to gas bubbles dissolving in solvents. In fact careful measurements of radius vs. time provide a ready means for finding the diffusivity of dissolved gases in liquids. For example, the diffusivities of H_2, O_2, N_2, He, Ne, A, and air in water[16] and oxygen in molten glass[14] have been obtained this way. The authors used several of the approximate solutions to eqn. (3), therefore their published diffusivities must be somewhat in error.

In contrast to studies of bubbles dissolving, the experimental study of bubbles growing as gas comes out of solution has not been undertaken until the present time. Studies are in progress at the University of Illinois using carbon dioxide in water. The gas is dissolved in the liquid at pressures of 2 to 4 atmospheres at $25°$ C. A sudden release of pressure causes uniform supersaturation, and bubbles appear. Growth is recorded by motion picture photography.

Preliminary tests[17] showed that homogeneous nucleation, that is nucleation in the body of a dust-free pool of liquid, could not be achieved. When the pressure was dropped to atmospheric, bubble formation began always on the walls of the container or on microscopic specks of suspended particulate matter. All growth data were obtained for bubbles on the walls.

A sample of the data are given in Fig. 4. Different contact angles are indicated for each bubble. Different angles for different runs were obtained deliberately by using various kinds of surface coatings, such as stearic acid, on the metal walls. The experimental values of the growth coefficient β, defined by eqn. (4), are 2.56 for Bubble 11 and 1.98 for Bubble 7. These values are close to theoretical values

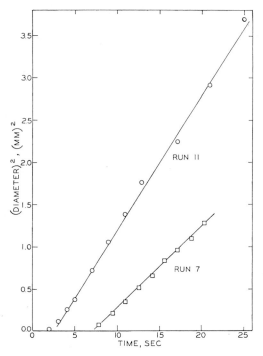

Fig. 4. Growth of CO_2 bubbles in water after pressure release. Run 7: Average contact angle = 50 degrees, pressure change from 43.2 to 14.2 p.s.i. abs. Run 11: Average contact angle = 78 degrees, pressure change from 55.9 to 14.4 p.s.i. abs.

from Scriven's solutions of 2.68 and 2.00, respectively. The extent of agreement between experiment and theory is interesting and surprising. True radial symmetry was assumed in the theory; it was impossible in the tests. The tests suggest that the effect of nearby walls may not always be severe.

BOILING MIXTURES

Although a number of theoretical papers are concerned with the growth of bubbles in boiling liquids[7, 8, 9], all but two treat pure liquids only. SCRIVEN[2] and

References p. 53–54

BRUIJN[18] considered binary mixtures. These two writers decided that mass diffusion and heat diffusion both were important and proceeded to solve eqns. (2) and (3) simultaneously. Bruijn dropped out the convection terms; Scriven left them in. Eqn. (1) was discarded, implying either that all mechanical forces are unimportant during the bubble growth, or that it is impossible to know what boundary conditions to use in eqn. (1).

For a boiling binary mixture, bubble growth behavior, R vs. θ, cannot be computed in closed form from eqns. (2) and (3). Scriven arbitrarily selected eqn. (9) as being convenient and used a digital computer to get numerical values of β for two systems: glycol-water and glycerol-water at atmospheric pressure.

$$R = 2\beta \sqrt{\alpha_L \theta} \tag{9}$$

At the constant value of $T_\infty - T_{sat}$, the value of β predicted for glycerol-water mixtures is a monotonic function of the composition. But for glycol-water mixtures a striking result occurs. A minimum value of β is predicted to exist for a composition of about 5 weight % water. According to these calculations, bubbles should grow slower in this particular mixture than in either pure water or pure glycol at the same ΔT. The predicted slowing-down effect is a result of mass diffusion interacting with heat diffusion.

Bruijn arbitrarily selected an equation, equivalent to eqn. (4), as being suitable for boiling mixtures. He solved for the dependence of the coefficient on composition for water-ethanol, water-acetone, and 1-butanol-water. In no case was a monotonic function revealed. The results must be accepted with caution, however, because of the exclusion of mass and heat transfer by convection in Bruijn's calculations.

Two publications include laboratory data for bubbles growing in boiling mixtures. The ethylene glycol-water system was tested by BENJAMIN AND WEST-WATER[19] and the results may be compared to Scriven's solution. VAN WIJK AND VAN STRALEN[20] gave data for 4.1 weight % methyl-ethyl ketone in water at $\Delta T = 24°C$, but no theoretical results for this system are available for comparison.

Benjamin and Westwater obtained growth information photographically. The apparatus was somewhat unique and its details have been published[21]. The set-up shown in Fig. 5 was used routinely to photograph at 6000 frames per second with $3 \times$ enlargement on the film. A few scenes were photographed with $66 \times$ magnification while using 6000 frames per second, but these conditions were not needed for routine boiling tests. A selection of the motion pictures are available for loan[22].

An earlier study of bubble growth in pure liquids[4] suggested that the growth rate of a bubble is a function of the size of its nucleation site. Small sites for example seem to produce faster-growing bubbles than do larger sites. In order to prevent any confounding of data for bubbles from different sites, it was decided to use a single artificial site and to photograph bubbles formed there only.

Fig. 5. Equipment for high-speed photography through a microscope. The test cell, traversing mechanism, microscope, camera, and arc lamp are mounted on railroad rails embedded in concrete.

The artificial site is indicated in Fig. 6. The opening was a 0.004 inch hole which connected to a 0.04 by 0.04 inch cavity below the surface. The site was machined as a 2-piece plug which was then set flush in a 0.125 inch hole in the copper heat-transfer surface. The final surface was electroplated copper, highly polished. All other pits or scratches were much smaller than 0.004 inch. This pit, obviously a good gas trap, was an excellent site. Literally millions of bubbles formed there during the months the site was in use.

The actual radius *vs.* time data were first tested with the arbitrary expression, eqn. (10),

$$R = a\theta^n \tag{10}$$

to see if the square-root of time relationship assumed by Scriven is correct. The method of least squares was used to find the best n (and a) for each bubble. Fig. 7 shows sample data for two bubbles. For the bubble having $T_w - T_{sat} = 18.1°$ C, the best value of n is 0.35. The bubble with $\Delta T = 4.3°$ C happened to be a vibrating bubble—many of these were seen. For this bubble the best fit corresponds to $n = 0.32$.

Therefore, the Scriven prediction of $n = 0.50$ is not correct for the test conditions used. In fairness it must be repeated that the Scirven solution is for uniform

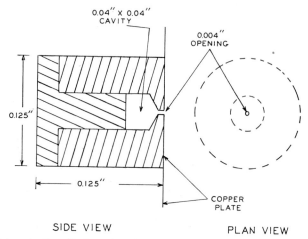

Fig. 6. Artificial nucleation site in a plug set in the heat-transfer surface. Bubbles formed here during boiling.

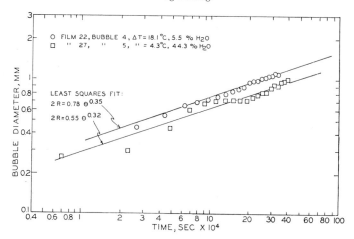

Fig. 7. Bubble growth data for glycol-water binary mixtures showing normal behavior (upper line) and a vibrating bubble (lower line).

original superheat and true spherical symmetry. The tests were carried out with a temperature gradient at the start and with bubbles at a pit on a wall. Exact quantitative correspondence between the theory and the data should not be expected. However, if mass diffusion is important for mixtures, it should affect

References p. 53–54

the phenomenon of bubble growth on hot walls as well as for bubbles suspended in superheated liquids. But since the real bubbles do not have $n = 0.5$, a comparison of bubbles for different compositions of water-glycol requires some arbitrary basis. One method is to compare values of a from eqn. (10). This method was used as shown in Fig. 8 and seems to show a minimum value in this coefficient for the

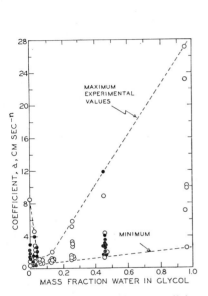

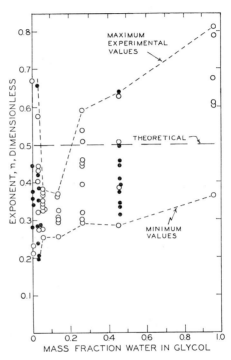

Fig. 8. Effect of composition on coefficient in eqn. (10), for glycol-water mixtures at $\Delta T = 18°C$. At any composition the open symbols and solid symbols show data obtained on two different days.

Fig. 9. Experimental data for exponent in eqn. (10), for glycol-water mixture at $\Delta T = 18°$ C. The symbols have the meaning stated in Fig. 8.

mixture of 5% water in glycol. A reasonable objection to this comparison is that a is a dimensional number whose dimensions depend on the numerical value of the empirical exponent n. The values of n can be compared for different compositions, as shown in Fig. 9. Again a minimum at about 5% water is evident. An alternate, and possibly sounder method of comparing growth rates is to force the R vs. θ data for each bubble to fit eqn. (9) as well as possible (that is, use $n = 0.5$ exactly) and thereby get estimates for the dimensionless coefficient β. Values of β obtained in this way are shown in Fig. 10. Again the prediction of a minimum growth rate for a composition of about 5% water in glycol is valid.

References p. 53–54

UNRESOLVED PROBLEMS

Wall Effect

Our understanding of bubble growth has a number of serious deficiencies. The greatest weakness is probably that concerned with the wall effect. Most theoretical works are concerned with perfect spherical symmetry. In real life, bubbles rarely grow according to this requirement. Real life bubbles are nearly always on solid walls. Exceptions are few.

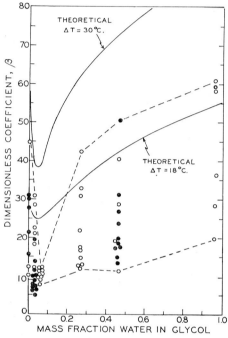

Fig. 10. Dimensionless growth-coefficient data compared to Scriven's prediction, glycol-water mixtures at $\Delta T = 18°$ C. The symbols have the meaning stated in Fig. 8.

Fig. 11 is one illustration of the wall effect for the growth of a hydrogen bubble during electrolysis[15]. The growth curve, plotted here as diameter *vs.* the square root of time, is composed of two straight lines. The change in slope occurs as the bubble contact angle undergoes a change from about 60 to 30 degrees. Motion pictures show that the contact angle for a single bubble is frequently variable during its growth. The contact area between a bubble and a wall is more or less constant at times, during which the bubble volume increases considerably, but this is followed often by a very sudden increase in the contact area. A definite stick-and-slip behavior is the result.

References p. 53–54

Rapid changes in the slope of curves (R *vs. θ*) for collapsing bubbles are described by HOUGHTON *et al.*[16]. Although these authors did not remark on the contact angle, they did note 'small changes in shape' of the bubbles during collapse. Their bubbles were small ($R < 0.25$ mm) and for that reason must have been segments of spheres. In such case a change in shape means a change in contact angle.

The bubble referred to in Fig. 2 did not exhibit sizable changes in growth rate. These bubbles had very small contact angles, near 10 degrees. For this contact

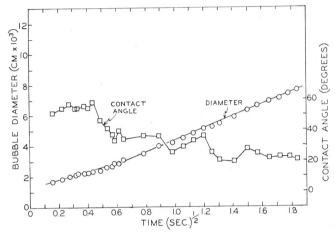

Fig. 11. Effect of contact angle on growth rate for hydrogen bubble during electrolysis of 0.1 N H$_2$SO$_4$ with constant current to platinum electrode.

angle the major and minor diameters are in a ratio of 1 to 0.993. This shape is so close to that of a complete sphere that a modest amount of stick and slip may be unimportant.

Fig. 12 shows how the liquid-gas interfacial area for a spherical segment containing a constant volume of gas varies as the contact angle is changed. A perfect sphere corresponds to a contact angle of zero and an ordinate value of unity. For angles near zero the interfacial area is a weak function of the angle. The dependence becomes much stronger for angles in the regions of about 30 to 60 degrees. Thus one obvious aspect of the wall effect, namely the influence of contact angle on the interfacial area available for mass transfer or heat transfer, will not be serious for small contact angles. It will not be serious either for angles near 90 degrees. The area effect can be serious for angles not close to zero or 90 degrees.

A second important aspect of the wall effect has to do with the liquid flow pattern during bubble expansion or contraction. Perfect radial flow, the case treated by mathematical workers, can exist for two situations only: a spherical bubble far away from any wall, or a perfect hemisphere on a frictionless wall.

References p. 53–54

The spherical model is referred to by many writers and is the one for which eqns. (1) to (3) were set up. Solutions for these equations are applicable to hemispheres provided the right simplifications are assumed. For example Scriven's solutions for isolated spheres apply to hemispheres on a frictionless wall if the starting liquid has a uniform superheat or supersaturation. On the other hand, if a gradient exists near the solid wall, a different approach must be used. Griffith[23] and Forster[24] for example treat the cases of hemispherical bubbles in a liquid

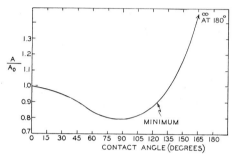

Fig. 12. Gas-liquid interfacial area for spherical-segment bubbles of constant volume on a solid wall.

having a linear temperature gradient or exponential temperature gradient near the solid wall. Other temperature and concentration profiles in the liquid may be chosen, and solutions for the growth of hemispherical bubbles can be obtained by numerical techniques.

Hemispheres do not represent the majority of real bubbles. For non-hemispheres on a wall, what is the theoretical growth behavior? This problem is unsolved.

One limiting case seems solvable, namely that for a perfect sphere tangent to a wall. The conduction equation for this case, ignoring transport by liquid flow, has been solved already. Liebermann[25] points out that the conduction solution differs from that for the case of true radial symmetry by a simple factor, ln 2. Hopefully, soon the convection contribution will be available for the tangent sphere.

Equation of Motion

Solution for the heat and mass balances coupled with the equation of motion are not yet available. Presumably, eqns. (1), (2), and (3) can be solved simultaneously using numerical methods on large digital computers. The solutions would contain many parameters and would be awkward to use. But until such solutions are carried out we are restricted to a consideration of some idealized, but unreal, physical properties. For example: liquids and gases of zero viscosity moving with zero inertia. We should be aware that physical situations may exist for which all three equations should be employed. The very early stages of bubble growth in boiling liquid mixtures is probably such a case.

Natural Variability

A number of experimental studies have been concerned with successive bubbles growing at single nucleation sites. These tests have included pure boiling liquids at natural sites[4, 26], pure boiling liquids at artificial sites[21], binary mixtures boiling at artificial sites[21], electrolytic bubbles at natural sites[10, 15, 27], gas dissolution on natural sites in depressurized liquids[17], and also gas dissolution at artificial sites in depressurized liquids. In no case did two successive bubbles grow exactly alike, even if generous allowance for experimental error is assumed. The situation is well demonstrated in Fig. 10. Each point in a vertical row of data points represents the growth behavior of one of the bubbles in one motion picture reel covering a total time of less than 1 second. All these bubbles formed at the same nucleation site under constant imposed test conditions. The deviation between replicate bubbles amounts to a few percent only for some of the tests, however deviations as large as 30% are not rare.

One explanation of the variability is suggested by the schlieren motion pictures of Hsu and Graham[28]. These films showed that bubbles formed during boiling grow in a thermal boundary layer on the wall of the heater. Each bubble break-off ruptures the boundary layer and sets up tiny eddies in the liquid. A new bubble does not appear until the boundary layer is re-established. This rebuilding process is an unsteady-state phenomenon and seems to be influenced by the size and shape of the eddies which arise at break-off. Put another way, the boundary layer grows in a turbulent field.

Variability is a nuisance, but nothing worse. It demands that future studies of bubble growth or collapse (at least if on walls) must employ proper statistical methods. A start in this direction has been made (Ref. 4 for example). Measurements on one bubble cannot be generalized with confidence. Some experimental workers have not been aware of this fact.

Bubble Interference

All existing mathematical analyses of bubble growth or collapse deal only with isolated bubbles. But in fact, many bubbles close to one another can grow or collapse in a liquid. Two growing bubbles close to one another compete for the same solute, during diffusion-controlled growth, and therefore must interact on one another. An analytical approach to this problem is complicated by the liquid flow pattern which is induced by the change of phase. Consider as an example a liquid with a non-uniform distribution of solute. Imagine two near-by bubbles growing simultaneously, one in a region of high concentration of solute and one in a region of low concentration. As the first bubble expands it may shove liquid of high concentration toward the second bubble. The second bubble could then increase its growth rate—an opposite effect to what would occur if the bubbles were far apart.

A few tests have been made to investigate bubble interference during electrolysis[10, 15]. For two bubbles of roughly equal size, no interference could be detected when the center-to-center spacing was greater than 1.9 bubble diameters. For smaller spacing interference caused either growth retardation or a growth speed-up. The data are not sufficient to show which will occur under stated conditions. This subject appears to be an interesting and fruitful field for future research.

ACKNOWLEDGMENT

Most of the experimental work was supported by a grant from the National Science Foundation.

NOTATION

(Dimensions in the $M\ L\ \theta\ T\ H$ System)

A gas-liquid interfacial area, L^2
A_0 surface area of perfect sphere, L^2
a empirical coefficient defined by eqn. (10), L/θ^n
C solute concentration, M/L^3
C_∞ solute concentration far away, M/L^3
C_{sat} solute concentration at saturation, M/L^3
C_L heat capacity of liquid, $H/(MT)$
D mass diffusivity, L^2/θ
k_L thermal conductivity of liquid, $H/(\theta LT)$
n empirical exponent defined by eqn. (10), dimensionless
P_i partial pressure of inerts in bubble, $M/(L\theta^2)$
P_v partial pressure of vapor in bubble, $M/(L\theta^2)$
P_∞ vapor pressure of liquid far away, $M/(L\theta^2)$
ΔP $P_v + P_i - P_\infty$
Q heat generated by distributed source, $H/(L^3\theta)$
R bubble radius, L
R_0 bubble radius at time zero, L
r radial coordinate in liquid, measured from bubble center, L
T temperature, T
T_∞ temperature of liquid far away, T
T_{sat} temperature of liquid at saturation, T
T_w wall temperature of heat source, T

References p. 53–54

ΔT temperature driving force, $T_w - T_{sat}$ or $T_\infty - T_{sat}$, T

α_L thermal diffusivity of liquid, L^2/θ

β coefficient defined by eqns. (4) or (9), dimensionless

ε $(\varrho_L - \varrho_v)/\varrho_L$, dimensionless

θ time, θ

λ latent heat of vaporization, H/M

μ_L viscosity of liquid, $M/(\theta L)$

ϱ_L density of liquid, M/L^3

ϱ_v density of vapor phase, M/L^3

σ surface tension, M/θ^2

Φ dimensionless group defined by eqn. (6)

REFERENCES

1 Lord Rayleigh, *Phil. Mag.*, 34 (1917) 94–98.

2 L. E. Scriven, *Chem. Eng. Sci.*, 10 (1959) 1–13.

3 L. E. Scriven, *Chem. Eng. Sci.*, 17 (1962) 55.

4 P. H. Strenge, Aluf Orell and J. W. Westwater, *A.I.Ch.E.J.*, 7 (1961) 578–583.

5 Paul Dergarabedian, *J. Fluid Mech.*, 9 (1960) 39–48.

6 E. E. Stanizewski, *Tech. Rept. No. 16, Div. of Sponsored Research*, Mass. Inst. Technol., Cambridge, Massachusetts, 1959.

7 M. S. Plesset, and S. A. Zwick, *J. Appl. Phys.*, 25 (1954) 493–500.

8 H. K. Forster and Novak Zuber, *J. Appl. Phys.*, 25 (1954) 474–478.

9 Garrett Birkhoff, R. S. Margulies and W. A. Horning, *Phys. Fluids*, 1 (1958) 201–204.

10 D. E. Westerheide, and J. W. Westwater, *A.I.Ch.E.J.*, 7 (1961) 357–362.

11 Takao Murakawa, *J. Electrochem. Soc. Japan*, 25, No. 5 (1957) p. E 61-E 62.

12 S. G. Bankoff, *Heat Transfer and Fluid Mech. Inst.*, Stanford Univ. Press, Stanford, California, 1956, pp. 1–13.

13 P. S. Epstein, and M. S. Plesset, *J. Chem. Phys.*, 18 (1950) 1505–1509.

14 R. H. Doremus, *J. Am. Ceram. Soc.*, 43 (1960) 655–61.

15 J. P. Glas, *M.S. Thesis*, Univ. of Illinois, Urbana, Illinois, 1962.

16 G. Houghton, P. D. Ritchie and J. A. Thomson, *Chem. Eng. Sci.*, 17 (1962) 221–227.

17 W. M. Buehl, *M.S. Thesis*, Univ. of Illinois, Urbana, Illinois, 1959.

18 P. J. Bruijn, *Physica*, 26 (1960) 326–334.

19 J. E. Benjamin and J. W. Westwater, *1961 International Heat Transfer Conference*, Boulder, Colorado, 1961, pp. 212–218.

20 W. R. Van Wijk and S. J. D. Van Stralen, *Physica*, 28 (1962) 150–171.

21 J. E. Benjamin and J. W. Westwater, *Proc. Fifth International Congress on High Speed Photography*, Washington, D.C., 1962, pp. 290–292.

22 J. W. Westwater and J. E. Benjamin, *Motion Picture, High-Speed Microscopic Study of Phase Changes*, Univ. of Illinois, Urbana, Illinois, 1960.

23 Peter Griffith, *Trans. Am. Soc. Mech. Engrs.*, 80 (1958) 721–727.

24 Kurt Forster, *Phys. Fluids*, 4 (1961) 448–455.

25 Leonard Liebermann, *J. Appl. Phys.*, 28 (1957) 205–211.

26 J. W. Westwater and P. H. Strenge, *Motion Picture, Active Sites and Bubble Growth During Nucleate Boiling*, Univ. of Illinois, Urbana, Illinois, 1958.

27 J. W. Westwater and D. E. Westerheide, *Motion Picture, Growth of Hydrogen Bubbles During Electrolysis*, Univ. of Illinois, Urbana, Illinois, 1960.

28 Yih-Yun Hsu and R. W. Graham, *Motion Picture, An Analytical and Experimental Study of the Thermal Boundary Layer and Ebullition Cycle in Nucleate Boiling*, Natl. Aeron. and Space Admin., Lewis Res. Center, Cleveland, Ohio, 1961 *(Suppl. to NASA Tech. Note D-594)*.

Supercavitating Flows and
Practical Applications

Hydronautics, Incorporated, Laurel, Maryland

CAVITATION AND VENTILATION

I propose to discuss cavity flows produced by moving bodies. These bodies are meant to be idealizations of things like lifting hydrofoil wings, or the symmetric struts which connect these wings through the ocean surface to the boat hull, or of a rotating and advancing screw propeller. These various cavity flows may be naturally formed as the result of vaporous cavitation or they may be formed as the result of the accidental or contrived introduction of a non-condensible gas such as air into the flow. In the latter case we speak when we are careful of a ventilated flow, or on rare occasions of gaseous cavitation. In haste we commonly speak of both vaporous and gaseous cavity flows as supercavitating—just as was done in the title of this paper. No confusion should be made in practice between these flows, for they have upon close examination their own unique features.

For practical purposes ventilated flows are highly interesting in that they may be caused to exist at much lower speeds and higher fluid pressures than vaporous cavity flows. The foils and struts on contemplated high speed hydrofoil craft (over 60 kts.) will be ventilated to the atmosphere and will not truly cavitate, while the propeller will be cavitating heavily and thereby operating in cavity flow.

Ventilated cavities must be continuously supplied with gas which is being continuously entrained by the unsteady flow in the region of collapse at the rear of the cavity and then convected downstream, Figs. 1 and 2. It seems reasonable that the amount of gas entrained should depend mainly on the flow at cavity collapse and that the rate of gas volume entrainment should therefore be approximately proportional to the volume flow in the hypothetical re-entrant jet. Recent hydrofoil data[1] seem to confirm this idea. An approximate value of the constant of proportionality is 0.5. A great deal of this entrained gas would seem to be delivered within the cavity to its rear through friction entrainment caused by the

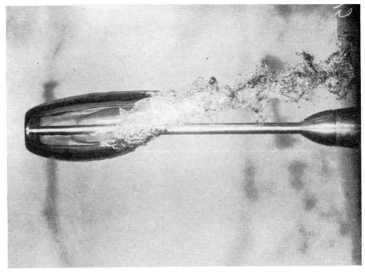

(Courtesy David Taylor Model Basin)

(Courtesy California Institute of Technology)
Fig. 1. Ventilated flow about discs.

(Courtesy David Taylor Model Basin)
Fig. 2. Ventilated flow about a hydrofoil.

References p. 78–79

large relative speed between the fluid outside and the gas inside the cavity, especially in the case where the Reynolds number is sufficiently high to insure a turbulent boundary layer in the gas flow at the fluid-gas interface. Ventilated cavities may enter into self-excited volume oscillations, as I shall discuss later, and when this happens large portions of the cavity at the rear may become periodically detached, whereupon the entrainment rate is of course very much increased[2].

The amount of gas needed to be supplied to a ventilated flow is of considerable importance to know, particularly as this gas may have to be supplied via an

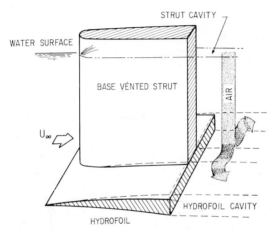

Fig. 3. Base vented strut-supercavitating hydrofoil configuration.

internal plumbing system as in the case of a ventilated propeller. For some contemplated hydrofoil systems air is naturally supplied to the foil through the cavity-trough created by the blunt-based strut which pierces the water surface. This clever utilization of a natural engineering structure was first accomplished by JOHNSON[3] at the NASA and forms an important basis for our optimistic expectations for high speed hydrofoil systems. The idea is illustrated in Fig. 3 and in Fig. 4 which shows such a system undergoing tests in a high speed facility at the Langley Laboratory of the NASA. Unfortunately the natural path of the air from atmosphere to foil is sometimes obstructed by the tendency to closure of the thin spray sheet thrown aft and up from the strut-water intersection. This spray closure is probably due to the Bernoulli suction caused by the gas flowing down through the trough behind the strut. The speed of this gas is not to be underestimated, for tests on a particular foil system indicate that supersonic gas speeds might result for foil speeds of about 100 kts. (Ref. 4). The net result of the surface closure is to reduce below atmospheric the pressures in the cavity behind the

Overhead camera

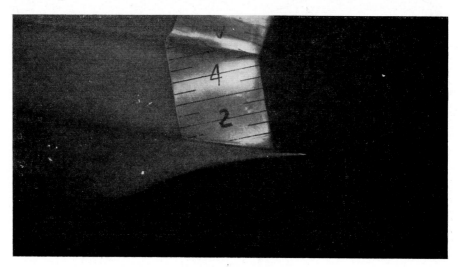

Underwater camera   (*Courtesy NASA*)
Fig. 4. Fully ventilated hydrofoil system.

strut and over the foil, and this tends to degrade the system efficiency. Various remedies such as spray strips or air jets are possible. The phenomena is reminiscent of cavity closure during water entry of projectiles[5] and indicates the possible importance of gas density scaling for certain ventilated hydrofoil experiments. Fig. 5 shows the same wing system as in Fig. 4 but with spray closure. Note the shortness of the strut cavity at the water intersection and the tendency of the foil cavity to close sooner due to the lower pressures.

INTERSECTION OF
WATER SURFACE

HYDROFOIL
LEADING EDGE

Overhead camera

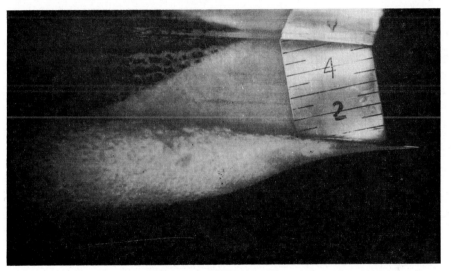

Underwater camera   (*Courtesy NASA*)

Fig. 5. Ventilated hydrofoil system with spray closure.

STRUTS

The blunt based support struts in high speed hydrofoil systems must be thick
enough to carry drive shafts for the propellers, and to house vertical flaps and
their actuators, and must be strong enough to carry the side loads generated
during turns. At the same time the power required to push the struts through
the water and to carry their weight must be minimized. The cavity drag of the
strut plays an important role in this situation. Similar remarks may be made about

References p. 78–79

base vented pods such as may form the intersection between foils and struts. The entire problem has been well discussed[6].

With this background to incite our interest let us look at the theory of cavity flow past struts, particularly to introduce a cavity flow involving two distinct free streamlines at different pressures and which in some cases produce cavity flows of zero drag.

It has previously been demonstrated[7,8] though the use of the Hydrodynamic

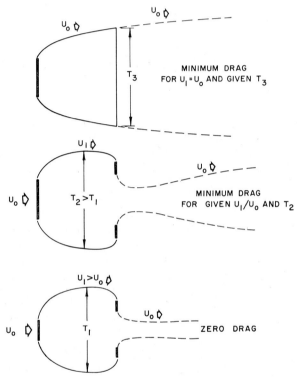

Fig. 6. Minimum drag bodies.

Comparison Theorem[9,10] that the planar or axially symmetric body of minimum cavity drag for a given thickness or volume, the length being fixed and the pressure coefficient nowhere negative on the body and zero in the wake, is the body cast by a flat normal plate or circular disk in Helmholtz flow (infinite wake), as illustrated in Fig. 6 at the top. For slender bodies this optimum body is indistinguishable from simple parabolas[6,8]. Superior as their resistance quality is to other shapes such as wedges, the use of parabolic struts in foil systems often involves the introduction of considerable cavity drag. In reality, although the pressure coefficient in the ventilated trailing cavity, $-\sigma_c$, may be sensibly zero, negative pressure coefficients may be sustained on the strut sides as long as their magnitude does not exceed that of the vapor cavitation number, σ_v. This fact gives rise to the following theoretical question:

What is the shape of the plane or axially symmetric body of minimum cavity drag for a given thickness or volume, the length being fixed, and whereon the speed nowhere exceeds a value U_1, while the speed on the wake boundary is identically equal to the speed at infinity?

The desired shape in answer to this question is, as long as such a flow exists, the flow formed by a flat plate (or disc) nose separated by the length of the body from two symmetrically located flat plates (or an annular disc) connected by a free streamline at speed U_1, and shedding from the interior edges of the rear plates (or annular disc) an infinite free streamline of velocity U_0, as shown in Fig. 6 center. The proof again lies in the application of the Hydrodynamic Comparison Theorem.

For slender bodies it can be shown[6] that for a given ratio U_1/U_0 the drag of this optimum body becomes zero for a sufficiently small thickness, as in Fig. 6 bottom, and no bodies of this shape seem to exist for lesser prescribed thicknesses. However, many other bodies of identically zero drag and satisfying the conditions of the problem exist for these lesser thicknesses. The existence of these latter zero drag bodies was first specifically discussed in Ref. 11.

Neither the exact nor the slender body version of this optimum body is realistic, in that too great adverse pressure gradients exist at the body trailing edge and would certainly lead to boundary layer separation there; however an alleviation of this pressure jump is easily arranged by a slight reshaping of the strut or pod. Low drag struts and pods utilizing these theoretical ideas have been successfully tested.

LINEARIZED THEORY

The linearized or small perturbation theory for supercavitating flows is carrying the burden of providing the kind of detailed information on cavity flows that engineering demands require and its family tree is spreading its branches in all directions, Fig. 7. In the case of infinite length cavities the linearized theory result has commonly been represented as the first order term in an expansion of the exact solution in powers of the strut thickness or hydrofoil camber and this has recently been conclusively shown[12] in the course of second order theory development. It is well known but should nevertheless be mentioned that this expansion is not uniformly convergent and that the first order or linearized solution possesses singularities which must be diplomatically dealt with—in the elegant manner, for instance, of LIGHTHILL[13].

References p. 78–79

The versatility of linearized theory is considerably enhanced by the fact that it permits solutions involving finite length closed cavities without the introduction of special artifices such as the re-entrant jet or Riabouchinsky symmetrization. For this good fortune we have to thank those very singularities which are ordinarily the curse of first order theory. The question was naturally early raised as to the connection between the linearized finite cavity solution and the various non-linear models. The evidence seemed to point to the re-entrant jet theory as the father of this singular child; the Riabouchinsky and Roshko models certainly

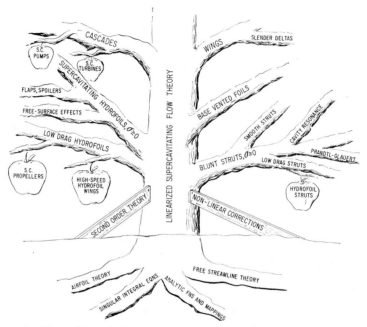

Fig. 7. Linearized supercavitating flow theory, family tree.

seemed to possess the wrong markings. Recent work by GUERST[14] does indeed show that the first order term in an expansion of the re-entrant jet solution is identical with the linearized theory solution. The re-entrant jet thickness is proportional to the cavity drag, which is in turn proportional to body thickness squared, and the re-entrant jet cavity thus closes to first order, making the existence of closed finite linearized cavities as a limiting re-entrant jet flow entirely plausible. Finally, it should be noted that more than one non-linear model may possess the same first order solution; the model of Weinig, for instance, which involves the termination of the free streamlines in a spiral type singularity seems another good candidate.

In the solution of steady finite cavity problems using linearized theory, it has generally been assumed from the beginning[15] that the condition of cavity closure should be utilized. The cavity drag experienced by a real supercavitating body must be manifested through momentum losses in the wake behind the body and its cavity, in much the same way as friction and form drag in a fully wetted flow

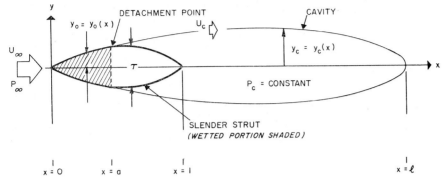

Fig. 8. Supercavitating flow past a slender strut.

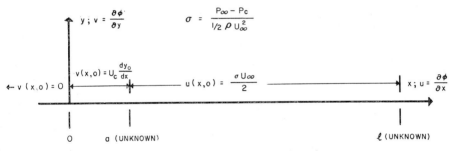

Fig. 9. Linearized boundary value problems for strut.

ϕ is harmonic and symmetric about $y = 0$. Cavity closure condition: $\int_0^l v(x, 0) \, dx = 0$.

Continuous slope and curvature at detachment: $\dfrac{dy_0(a)}{dx} = \dfrac{dy_c(a)}{dx}$, $\dfrac{d^2y_0(a)}{dx^2} = \dfrac{d^2y_c(a)}{dx^2}$

manifest themselves. It seems fair to consider the effect of these momentum wakes through their representation in terms of tail-like source distributions; the closure condition is thereby upset, but only to second order since the drag and thus the source strengths representing the wakes are of this order. The closure condition thus seems valid within the framework of linearized theory.

The mathematics of the planar linearized theory of supercavitating flows has involved two major techniques, both leading nicely to solutions in terms of quadratures. One of these involves the phrasing of the problem directly in terms of a Cauchy-type singular integral equation and the inversion thereof. This is the method utilized in the original treatment of blunt struts with finite trailing cavity[15].

I believe the only original aspects of the mathematics involved there is that the integral equation statement is made over an interval whose length (the cavity length) is initially unknown, but must be determined from a side integral condition (the closure condition). In the case of smooth struts with smooth detachment an additional parameter (the detachment position) is initially unknown too and must be determined from a point condition on the solution (continuous curvature at detachment)[16]. The reduction of this strut problem to a boundary value problem is illustrated in Figs. 8 and 9. The integral equation for the cavity shape y_c arises through the expression of u in the interval $a - l$ as an integral of Cauchy type over the interval $o - l$ involving an unknown integrand proportional to v in that interval.

The original treatment of arbitrary lifting hydrofoils trailing infinite cavities and of flat plate foils with finite cavities introduces the second important mathematical aspect[8, 17]. In these cases the analytical nature of the complex perturbation velocity, $u-iv$, was made use of in order first to transform the boundary conditions from a non-symmetric statement on a finite or semi-infinite slit into a symmetric statement on a half plane. Thereafter solutions were forthcoming, often in terms of already available solutions for the quantities on the half plane and sometimes for the desired analytic function almost directly by inspection. The technique of first-step mapping has by now been much resorted to, although not always into a half plane.

FOILS

The first linearized treatment of lifting hydrofoils allowed an interpretation of the forces on the hydrofoil in terms of those acting on an equivalent thin airfoil, thus immediately giving rise to important conclusions regarding the shape of foils of optimum performance. An important element in the operation of a supercavitating hydrofoil is the requirement to maintain the upper surface entirely within the cavity and thus to reduce friction drag, and a very considerable effort has been directed toward the determination of optimum foils including considerations of strength and friction drag as well as of the cavity or form drag accompanying the production of lift. The very high structural loadings which accompany operation at high speeds in water cause stress to be given the importance of structural considerations and thus very much complicates the actual design of practical foils[18]. The principal behind the achievement of low cavity drag for a given lift is easily stated, however, in terms of creating a counterthrust on the forward portion of the concave bottom and thus opposing the drag experienced by the rearward portion of the concave bottom, as illustrated in Fig. 10; this must, of course, be accomplished without causing cavitation to occur anywhere on the foil bottom or causing the foil upper surface to become wetted. A variety of foil shapes which have been tested, but not all of which are really satisfactory are shown in Fig. 11. Note particularly on the lowermost foil the use of a so-called annex which hides itself entirely within the cavity, thus not affecting the hydrodynamic performance, but contributing at the same time in an important way to spanwise bending strength. In order to emphasize the importance of structural considerations a wing experiencing leading edge flutter is shown in Fig. 12.

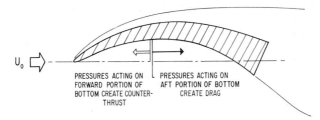

Fig. 10. The principle of low drag foil design.

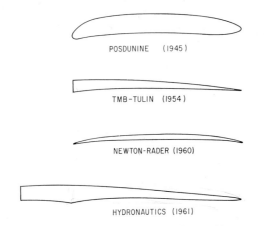

Fig. 11. Supercavitating propeller profiles.

In practice the application of planar theory to the design of three dimensional objects such as propellers or hydrofoil wings involves many complications such as those due to three dimensional effects or interferences between wing and the ocean surface, or between a blade and the cavity shed from the blade preceding. The latter effects have to a certain extent been dealt with by the application of planar theory to the consideration of lifting hydrofoils operating parallel to and beneath (hydrofoil wing) or above (propeller blade) a free surface; the connection between the latter problem and the flow about a supercavitating propeller will perhaps be made evident by Fig. 13. The effects of parallel free surfaces on hydro-

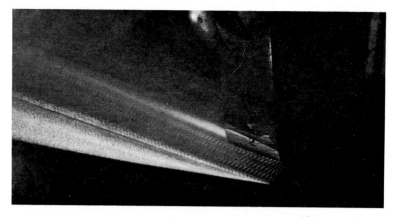

(*Courtesy NASA*)
Fig. 12. Ventilated hydrofoil with leading edge flutter.

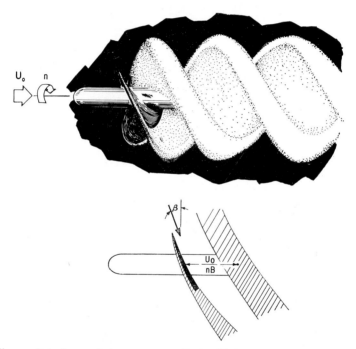

Fig. 13. Interference between supercavitating blade and neighboring cavity.

foil performance at zero cavitation number (infinite cavity) can again easily be reduced to a problem involving quadratures by the first-step application of a complex velocity mapping in order to transform the ocean surface plus the semi-infinite hydrofoil-slit onto a half plane; the Schwartz-Christoffel transformation is

appropriate. This mapping technique is illustrated in Fig. 14. As may be physically
clear, the supercavitating hydrofoil wing of given shape receives an augmentation
of lift, and its cavity thickens, as it approaches a free surface from below, while a
supercavitating propeller blade of given shape suffers a loss in thrusting ability,
and its cavity thins, as the spacing between the blade and its neighboring cavity
decreases. These interference effects are extremely important in practice.

The fully submerged foil systems on a high speed hydrofoil boat are complicated

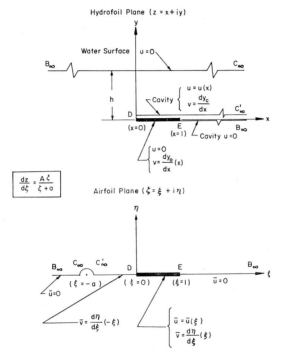

Fig. 14. The linearized version of a hydrofoil near a free surface
transformed into its equivalent airfoil; $\sigma = 0$.

in that they may have to carry flaplike devices in order to make possible take-off
at reasonable speeds, to provide for suitable stability and control, and to annul
the loads imposed by the waves. A schematic wing of Hydronautics design is
shown in Fig. 15. The performance of both lower surface flaps and upper surface
(or spoiler) flaps has been studied with the aid of linearized theory, including
the effect of a free surface[19, 20]; in addition the performance of a jet flap on a
supercavitating plate in an infinite medium has been treated[21]. The latter leads
to an interesting boundary value problem in that the boundary condition on the
lower cavity is stated in terms of a relationship between u and v'. This problem is

again solved through a first-stage mapping of the complex velocity onto a half plane and the subsequent use of suitably modified mathematics previously developed to deal with integral equations arising in the treatment of completely wetted airfoils with jet flaps[22].

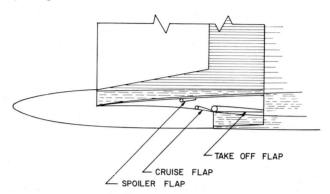

Fig. 15. High-speed wing system.

DELTA WINGS

The three dimensional effects involved in the flow about most practical super-cavitating wings are generally treated by applying so-called lifting line and lifting surface corrections to two-dimensional theoretical results[3] and this procedure has worked well in practice. In the case of slender delta wings with flat bottoms a theory was provided a few years ago which predicted the existence of partial cavities springing from the wing's sharp and highly swept leading edges; the flow pattern over the wing being conical[23]. The extent of the cavities depends, according to the theory, on a similarity parameter $\sigma/\alpha\beta$, where α is the wing angle of attack and β the apex angle of the delta wing. Even for vanishing σ the cavities in this conical flow cannot close, but there must always exist a kind of re-entrant jet flow along the centerline of the delta. These conical flows past delta wings, whether slender or not, have been observed and just this year reported on[24]. Photographs of the flow past a 45° delta wing are shown in Fig. 16; vaporous cavitation is occurring. These experiments seem to confirm at least qualitative aspects of the linearized theory. Note particularly in the figure, the re-entrant jet type of flow occurring along the delta centerline at the lowest cavitation number. The theoretical treatment of this problem involved the use of slender body theory as distinct from two dimensional perturbation theory, and an important consequence of the theory required that the outflow of fluid in the transverse plane caused by the continual streamwise growth of the cavity cross-section be exactly compensated for by an inflow of fluid between the cavities; this inflow was imagined to go into

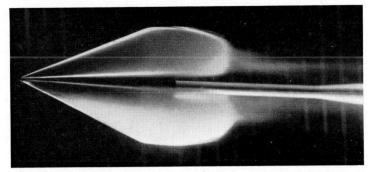

$\alpha = 10°, \sigma = 0.18$

$\alpha = 10°, \sigma = 0.10$

$\alpha = 5°, \sigma = 0.18$

(*Courtesy Max-Planck-Institut für Strömungsforschung*)

Fig. 16. Supercavitating flow about a delta wing (apex angle 45°).

two symmetrically placed re-entrant jets under each of the cavities. Thus even linearized theories are not *always* immune of the necessity to invoke re-entrant jets.

FINITE LENGTH EFFECTS IN PLANAR FLOWS

Our understanding of the effects of finite cavity lengths, that is, of cavitation number on the forces acting on planar bodies, was very much enhanced through linearized theory results[8, 15, 25]. At one time and not so long ago, as I recall, most engineers believed that the drag on a symmetric body might be closely approximated by the simple rule $C_D(\sigma) = C_D(0) [1 + \sigma]$ while the lift on a hydrofoil followed from $C_L(\sigma) = C_L(0) + \sigma$. We now know that these approximations may

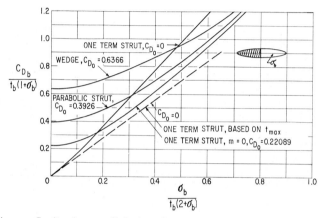

Fig. 17. Cavity drag coefficient *vs.* base cavitation number parameter.

be quite misleading. The way in which forces vary with σ depends very much on the nondimensional cavity length, which in turn depends for reasonably slender bodies on the ratios $\bar{t}(2 + \sigma)/\sigma$ for struts and $\alpha(2 + \sigma)/\sigma$ for foils, where $\bar{t}$ is the non-dimensional strut thickness and α the foil camber or angle of attack. These ratios may in fact be thought of as similarity parameters. For sufficiently large values of these parameters then, all of the forces on supercavitating planar bodies vary in proportion to the factor $[1 + \sigma]$. As the parameter decreases, the forces increase more rapidly with increasing σ. This effect is illustrated for the case of various strut shapes in Fig. 17; similar curves for the lift on a lifting hydrofoil might be shown with replacement of $\bar{t}$ by α. The minimum value of the similarity parameter $\bar{t}(2 + \sigma)/\sigma$ for which the $[1 + \sigma]$ factor rule applies is about 10, thus demonstrating the need for caution to be applied in the application of this rule. It may be useful to reconsider previously derived results explicitly in terms of the similarity parameter, as has been done here.

References p. 78–79

CAVITY RESONANCE

A new cavity flow phenomenon has recently been observed by SILBERMAN AND SONG[2,26] at the University of Minnesota. They have produced ventilated cavities which experience self-excited oscillations behind both lifting and non-lifting bodies in both a free-jet water tunnel and in a towing tank. Personnel at Hydronautics have recently considered the theory of unsteady cavity flows behind strut shapes at finite cavitation number and have been able to predict these cavity resonances and their general observed characteristics while further elucidating their complexities[27].

First of all, it is important to appreciate that the effects of compressibility must inevitably be considered in phrasing the problem of unsteady finite cavity flows. For small Mach number of the approaching flow, the wave equation for the velocity potential governs:

$$\nabla^2\phi - \frac{1}{a_\infty^2}\frac{\partial^2\phi}{\partial t^2} = 0$$

and this has the fundamental solution (source at the origin):

$$\phi(x, y, t) = \text{Re}\left[\frac{iA}{4} e^{i\omega t}H_0^{(2)}\left(\frac{\omega r}{a_\infty}\right)\right]$$

where Re denotes real part of, A is the source strength, ω is the frequency, $r^2 = x^2 + y^2$, and a_∞ is the speed of sound in the undisturbed gas. The asymptotic behavior of the Hankel function is:

$$H_0^{(2)}(r/\lambda) \rightarrow \begin{cases} \dfrac{2}{i\pi}\ln{(r/\lambda)} & \text{for } r/\lambda \ll 1 \\[2ex] \sqrt{\dfrac{2\lambda}{\pi r}}\, e^{i(r/\lambda - \pi/4)} & \text{for } r/\lambda \rightarrow \infty \end{cases}$$

where λ is the sound wave length for frequency ω.

Therefore, the potential for an oscillating source in even the most slightly compressible fluid vanishes identically at infinity in contrast to the idealized potential of incompressible theory. It is therefore unnecessary to be concerned about the mathematical unboundedness of the incompressible potential which arises when allowing volume oscillations of the cavity flow; I emphasize this since several past treatments of unsteady cavity flow have been so concerned—to the extent that a prohibition against cavity volume changes was specified. Such a prohibition makes impossible—to start with—the prediction of cavity resonance, which surely arises through an interchange of energy between the gas within the cavity and the fluid without, as in the case of oscillating stationary gas bubbles, and thus requiring pressure changes to occur in the gas.

For frequencies low enough to result in wavelengths many times the cavity length, as is very much the case here, the flow may be treated as incompressible, excepting conditions near infinity; this is verified by the small distance approximation to the Hankel function as given above, which is in the form of the incompressible potential. Following the solution of the incompressible problem the far field noise may, if desired, be estimated through the use of the large distance approximation to the Hankel function as given above.

The exact problem considered involves a stationary blunt based wedge in an infinite medium with a finite cavity in which the pressure is assumed to be pulsating about some mean pressure corresponding to the steady state cavity length involved. The cavity responds, of course, to these imposed pressure pulsations and the resonance condition corresponds to the case where these cavity oscillations can occur without a variation of the mass of gas within the cavity. The theory being linear the amplitudes of these oscillations are not predicted, but they are of substantial magnitude according to experiments.

The linearized theory is applied to the above problem invoking the closure condition, smoothness of the flow at the wedge trailing edge, and requiring that the specified boundary condition on the normal velocity on the wedge plus the specified pressure condition on the cavity be satisfied; proper account must, of course, be taken of the flow unsteadiness in specifying both the pressure condition on the cavity, and the closure condition. The length of the cavity was determined to vary only to the second order in the pressure pulsation so it could be assumed constant.

Various modes of resonance corresponding to discrete wave numbers in the cavity oscillation were found theoretically. These modes correspond to discrete frequencies non-dimensionalized in terms of cavity length and flow velocity. Two different regions of oscillation were found, corresponding to cavity lengths smaller and greater than a certain critical length. For wedges, this critical length is four times the wedge length. In each region a particular mode of resonance corresponds to a particular flow speed defined by a sort of critical pressure coefficient P^* defined as:

$$\sqrt{P^*} = (\varrho/\varrho_g)^{\frac{1}{2}} \frac{U_0}{a_g}$$

where ϱ is the fluid density, ϱ_g the gas density, U_0 the flow speed and a_g the speed of sound in the gas. Some theoretical results together with those from experiments in a free jet tunnel are shown in Table I. The effects of the tunnel boundaries have not been reflected in the theoretical results, but nevertheless the comparison is encouraging.

References p. 78–79

TABLE I

THEORETICAL AND EXPERIMENTAL* RESULTS

n = number of waves

$$k = \frac{\text{(frequency) (cavity length)}}{U_0}$$

n	1	2	3	4
k_{theory} $l_0 > 4$	8.4	14.8	21.5	27.4
$l_0 < 4$	5.5	11.8	18	24.2
$k_{\text{expt.}}$ ($\frac{1}{8}''$ normal plate)	4.5–6.1	9.9–13.0	14.2–19	17.1–22.9
$P^*_{\text{expt.}}$ ($\frac{1}{8}''$ normal plate)	2.26	1.25	0.818	0.631
$\dfrac{P_n^*}{P_1^*}$ (expt.)	1	0.55	0.36	0.28
$\dfrac{P_n^*}{P_1^*}$ (theory) $l_0 > 4$	1	0.505	0.29	0.23
$l_0 < 4$	1	0.536	0.38	0.30

* Experiments of SILBERMAN AND SONG

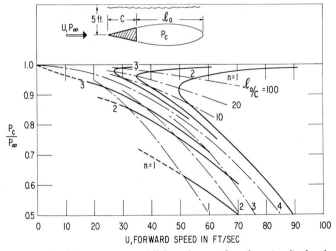

Fig. 18. Cavity resonance conditions for a 15° wedge at 5 ft. depth.

The theory has been applied to the case of a particular wedge and particular flow conditions and the resultant contours of resonant speeds and cavity pressure conditions are shown in Fig. 18. These calculations clearly show the existence of both a minimum and maximum speed for which resonance can occur in an isolated

References p. 78–79

flow. Speaking both literally and figuratively, more is certain to be heard of this interesting phenomenon.

SUPERCAVITATING PROPELLERS

The need to design propellers capable of operating at high forward speeds and at depths associated with surface ships and hydrofoil craft has caused great interest in supercavitating propellers. The subject is a very complex one, is fraught with difficulty, and is very far from completely understood. I wish here only to speak briefly concerning one aspect of the subject and in doing so to introduce a kind of cavity flow which has not, to my knowledge, previously been discussed. It concerns an axially symmetric flow, so that I cannot now be accused of entirely neglecting that subject, even though I have hitherto avoided it.

Each blade of a supercaviting propeller sheds a cavity in a helical sheet. The length and thickness of these cavities depends very much on the operating conditions of the propeller. A well-designed propeller operating near design conditions will generally shed a cavity of modest length and volume. A propeller operating at relatively low efficiency will shed larger cavities. A moderate case involving a two-bladed propeller is shown in Fig. 19.

At conditions far from design, as occurs for the propeller during the crucial take-off operation of a hydrofoil craft, the cavities shed by the blades may become monstrous as in the extreme case shown in Fig. 20; the propeller here is three bladed. It is evident in this case that the flow passing through the propeller plane is severely restricted by the cavities; in fact little flow would seem to be passing through. The thrust produced by the propeller is very much affected by the inflow conditions and it therefore becomes important to deal theoretically with the blockage caused to a flow by a finite supercavitating obstruction through which some flow passes. A screen or grid of circular planform and possessing a finite but large number of elements separated by spaces would comprise such an obstacle. The flow for some finite length behind the grid is imagined to be filled with the individual cavities shed by the grid elements plus rearward flowing jets of the fluid which passed through the grid face. The pressure in this entire bubble behind the grid is presumably very close to constant. I have considered this problem recently and have tried to estimate the bubble length and shape from a knowledge only of the cavitation number and cavity drag acting on the disc shaped grid. A rather strange boundary value problem presents itself, for unlike the case of cavity flow past a solid body, no boundary conditions representing the obstacle itself are involved; the value of cavity drag alone is presumably sufficient for this representation.

The cavities within the bubble may be represented by unknown distributions

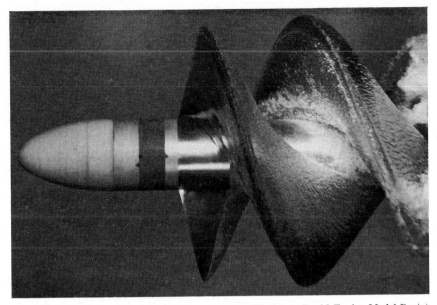

(*Courtesy David Taylor Model Basin*)

Fig. 19. Lightly loaded supercavitating propeller.

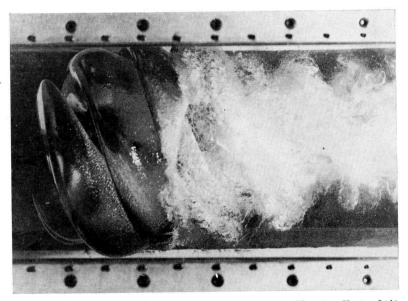

(*Courtesy Vosper Ltd.*)

Fig. 20. Heavily loaded supercavitating propeller.

of sources or axial doublets. I have simplified the problem of determining these distributions by assuming that they are uniform in any transverse plane through the bubble; only an axial distribution need then be determined.

A mathematical equivalence exists between the flow field due to a disc of uniform axial doublets and that due to a vortex ring circumscribing the disc. This equivalence is illustrated in Fig. 21. The flow α represents schematically that due

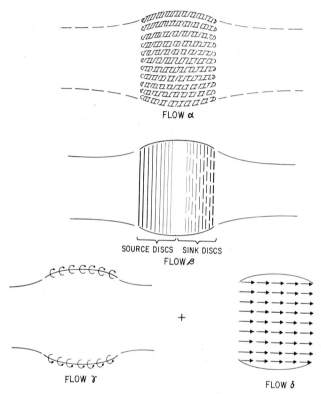

FLOW α

SOURCE DISCS   SINK DISCS
FLOW β

FLOW γ

+

FLOW δ

Fig. 21. Schematic of drag disc flow models.

to a circular grid of many elements and flow β is its idealization in terms of a continuous axial distribution of sources and sinks whose strength is assumed constant in each transverse plane. Flow γ is that past an axial distribution of vortex rings arranged on the outer surface of the bubble. Flow δ represents a purely axial flow which exists only within the bubble and which is uniform in any transverse plane but varies in the axial direction so as to make the superposition of flows γ and δ continuous at the bubble boundary. The mathematical equivalence earlier mentioned causes flow β to be identical with this superposition of γ and δ. Now only the axial ring vortex distribution need be calculated; this must be such as to cause the flow along the bubble boundary to be constant and appropriate to the cavity pressure. With the additional assumption that the ring vortices be considered as on a cylinder of constant radius, their distribution may be approximated making use of available results from the theory of thin annular airfoils[28], the length of the bubble being known.

The bubble length increases with cavity drag and remains to be determined.

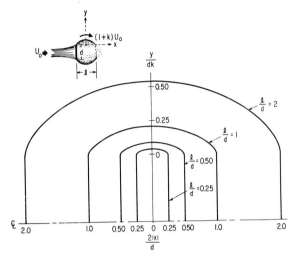

Fig. 22. Cavity shape behind axially symmetric supercavitating obstacle.

This can be done by making a momentum balance for each of flow β and γ using control surfaces at upstream infinity and midway through the bubbles. This allows the unknown flow along the central control plane outside of the bubble boundary, which flow is identical in β and γ, to be dealt with, and an equality results between the cavity drag acting on the face of the obstacle and some characteristics of the ring vortex distribution. The latter depend on the bubble length and the latter thus becomes related to cavity drag. Some calculated bubble shapes are shown in Fig. 22.

The extension of the kind of analysis described above to the case of a heavily cavitating propeller with many blades may also be carried out and yields interesting results in connection with propeller performance. One conclusion is particularly interesting. The cavity blockage decelerates the approach flow in opposition to the acceleration caused by the thrusting action of the propeller. For some operating conditions it turns out that the flow through the disc may actually be less than that far upstream quite in contrast to normal expectations, but as has, in fact, been observed in practice[29]. Much more remains to be learned of this and related phenomena which occur during the operation of supercavitating or ventilated propellers.

References p. 78–79

REFERENCES

1 F. R. Schiebe and J. M. Wetzel, Ventilated Cavities on Submerged Hydrofoils of Finite Span, *Tech. Memo. No. M-91*, St. Anthony Falls Hydraulic Lab., Univ. of Minn., July 1961.

2 E. Silberman and C. S. Song, Instability of Ventilated Cavities, *J. Ship Res.*, 5, No. 1 (1961) 13-33.

3 V. E. Johnson, The Influence of Submersion, Aspect Ratio and Thickness on Supercavitating Hydrofoils Operating at Zero Cavitation Number, *Proc. 2nd Symposium on Naval Hydrodynamics* (Gov't Printing Office), Washington, D.C., August 1958.

4 K. L. Wadlin, Ventilated Flows with Hydrofoils, NACA Contribution to the *12th General Meeting of the American Towing Tank Conference*, Berkeley, California, August 1959.

5 G. Birkhoff, *Hydrodynamics*, Princeton Univ. Press, 1950.

6 V. E. Johnson and S. E. Starley, The Design of Base-Vented Struts for High Speed Hydrofoil Systems, *Hydronautics Tech. Rept. 001-16*, September 1962.

7 J. Serrin, On Plane and Axially Symmetric Free Boundary Problems, *J. Rational Mech. Analysis*, 2 (1953) 563-575.

8 M. P. Tulin, Supercavitating Foils and Struts, *Proc. N.P.L. Symposium on Cavitation in Hydrodynamics* (Teddington, England 1955), Phil. Soc., N.Y.

9 M. Lavrentieff, On Certain Properties of Univalent Functions and Their Applications to Wake Theory, *Mat. Sb.*, 46 (1938) 391-458 (in Russian).

10 D. Gilbarg, Uniqueness of Axially Symmetric Flows with Free Boundaries, *J. Rational Mech. Analysis*, 1 (1952) 309-320.

11 A. G. Fabula, Application of Thin Airfoil Theory to Hydrofoil with Cut-Off Ventilated Trailing Edge, *Naval Ordnance Test Station TP 2547*, September 1960.

12 C. F. Chen, Second-order Supercavitating Hydrofoil Theory, *J. Fluid Mech.*, 13 (1962) 321-332.

13 M. J. Lighthill, A New Approach to Thin Aerofoil Theory, *Aeron. Quart.*, 3 (1951) 193.

14 J. A. Geurst, Linearized Theory of Two-Dimensional Cavity Flows, *Thesis*, Delft Tech. Inst., 1961.

15 M. P. Tulin, Steady Two Dimensional Cavity Flows about Slender Bodies, *DTMB Rept. 834*, 1953.

16 M. P. Tulin, New Developments in the Theory of Supercavitating Flows, *Proc. 2nd Symposium on Naval Hydrodynamics* (Gov't Printing Office), Washington, D.C., August 1958.

17 M. P. Tulin and M. P. Burkart, Linearized Theory for Flows about Lifting Foils at Zero Cavitation Number, *DTMB Rept. C-638*, 1955.

18 J. Auslaender, The Linearized Theory for Supercavitating Hydrofoils Operating at High Speeds near a Free Surface, *J. Ship Res.*, 6, No. 2 (1962) 8-23.

19 J. Auslaender, The Behaviour of Supercavitating Foils with Flaps Operating at High Speed near a Free Surface, *J. Basic Eng.*, D85 (1963).

20 C. F. Chen, Linearized Theory for Thin Supercavitating Hydrofoils with Spoiler Flaps Operating at High Speeds Beneath a Free Surface, *Hydronautics Tech. Rept. 119-1*, June 1961.

21 H. T. Ho, The Linearized Theory of a Supercavitating Hydrofoil with a Jet Flap, *Hydronautics Tech. Rept. 119-2*, June 1961.

22 D. A. Spence, The Lift Coefficient of a Thin, Jet-Flapped Wing, *Proc. Roy. Soc. (London)*, A 238 (1956) 46-68.

23 M. P. Tulin, Supercavitating Flow Past Slender Delta Wings, *J. Ship Res.*, 3, No. 3 (1959) 7-22.

24 H. Reichardt and W. Sattler, *Three-Component-Measurements on Delta Wings with Cavitation*, Rept. of the Max-Planck Inst. Strömungsforsch., Göttingen, July 1962.

25 T. Y. Wu, A Note on the Linear and Non-linear Theories for Fully Cavitated Hydrofoils, *Cal. Inst. Tech. Rept. No. 21-22*. August 1956.

26 C. S. Song, Pulsation of Ventilated Cavities, *J. Ship Res.*, 5, No. 4 (1962) 8-20.

27 C. C. HSU AND C. F. CHEN, On the Pulsation of Finite Ventilated Cavities, *Hydronautics Tech. Rept. 115–4*, November 1962.

28 D. KÜCHEMANN AND J. WEBER, *Aerodynamics of Propulsion*, McGraw-Hill, New York, 1953.

29 V. L. POSDUININ, The Theory of the Mechanism and Action of Supercavitating Propellers, *Bull. Acad. Sci. USSR (Dept. of Tech. Sci.)*, 10–11 (1945).

Cavitation in Hydrodynamic Lubrication

G. I. TAYLOR

Department of Physics, University of Cambridge, Cambridge, England

Cavitation or separation in the oil film of hydrodynamic lubrication has long been recognized as an important factor in the design of bearings. While engineers have exercised much ingenuity in trying to allow for it, little effort has been devoted to the study of the phenomenon itself. I think that this is due to three main reasons. The first is that a simple journal bearing is essentially a mechanism by which a rotating shaft can be supported against a lateral load, so that the geometry of the lubricating fluid depends on the load, as well as the peripheral speed, and the difference in radii between the shaft and the bearing. This leads to great complication in the analysis, which absorbs most of the attention of the workers in the subject.

The second is that it is very difficult to make experiments which can reveal the physical conditions that determine the position of the meniscus which separates the fully lubricated from the separated part of a lubrication film, particularly when the geometry of the solid surface is not predetermined—in nearly all the recorded experiments it is not.

A third reason is that in hydrodynamically lubricated bearings the fluid pressures in the high pressure parts are usually great compared with atmospheric pressure and with the pressure in the parts (if any) of the bearing where cavitation has occurred; and areas where the pressure is lower than that of the atmosphere make little contribution to the total reaction between bearing surface and shaft. Therefore, it is sufficient for most practical purposes to assume that the pressure is positive throughout.

The interest, even the practical interest, in cavitation or separation of viscous fluids flowing in narrow passages is not limited to its occurrence in lubrication theory. In other cases where great pressures do not occur surface tension may be of primary importance but it may justifiably be left out of consideration in most problems in lubrication theory.

In designing experiments to determine the physical character of the meniscus

References p. 101

separating a viscous lubricant from the outside air, it seems essential to reduce the number of variables. The first step is obviously to use predetermined geometry and to limit the motion to two dimensions. The simplest practical way to form a meniscus is to fill a cylindrical tube with viscous fluid and blow it out by air pressure applied at one end. The air forms itself into a column with a round end, which may be called the meniscus. This travels down the tube till it reaches the far end. After the meniscus has passed any point in the tube, the fluid which is left behind stays practically at rest because the viscosity of air is so much less than that of the fluid that the pressure in it is nearly constant along its length. The simplest measurement that can be made is the ratio m of the amount of fluid left behind to the internal volume of the tube. I have indeed made such measurements (TAYLOR[1], 1961). The main result is that, as would be expected on theoretical grounds, m depends only on the non-dimensional combination $\mu U/T$ where μ is viscosity, U the velocity of the meniscus relative to the wall of the tube, and T is surface tension. This may be expressed by the equation

$$m = F_1(\mu U/T). \tag{1}$$

When $\mu U/T$ is small, F_1 is small, but as $\mu U/T$ increases, F_1 appears to approach an asymptotic limit. In my experiments (TAYLOR[1], 1961), which extended up to $\mu U/T = 1.9$, m had risen to 0.56. In some later experiments by BRYAN COX[2], which were of this same type, m nearly reached 0.60 when $\mu U/T$ was 17.5. This point is mentioned here to show that the asymptotic value of m is *not* 0.50, as it would be if the criterion were that the bubble cannot go faster through the tube than the maximum fluid velocity in the Poiseille flow which is driven by the pressure in the bubble. The significance of this fact will appear later.

The other thing which could be measured is the difference in pressure between the fluid on the two sides of the meniscus. It was not possible to do this in my experiments but it is worthwhile considering the physical meaning of such measurements if they could be made. The flow far ahead of the meniscus is the Poiseille flow, which is associated with a uniform pressure gradient $(8/a^2)\mu U$, a being the radius of the bore of the tube.

To connect the pressure in the air column with the velocity of the meniscus, it would be necessary to know how the uniform pressure gradient in the fluid connects with the uniform pressure in the air. The sketch of Fig. 1 explains what is needed. AOB is the air bubble, Ox is the axis of symmetry of the bubble, and Oy the radial co-ordinate. The distribution of pressure along the axis is represented on an axial plane Oxy by the line CEFOx, and the pressure which would have existed at the vertex O of the bubble if the uniform gradient which exists in the fluid far away from it had been continued up to the vertex is represented by D. Though it is a difficult matter to calculate the flow near the vertex, all that is necessary to connect the pressure in the air with the flow in the tube is the pressure difference δp represented by OD, and since there is only one non-dimensional variable, $\mu U/T$, in the problem, it seems that the pressure change δp must be representable by an expression of the form

$$\delta p = -\frac{\mu U}{a} F_2 \left(\frac{\mu U}{T}\right). \tag{2}$$

It will be seen that to calculate how fast fluid would be blown out of a tube by a given pressure, both F_1 and F_2 must be known; but since F_2 is likely to be comparable with 1 when $\mu U/T$ is large and must tend to $2/(\mu U/T)$ when $\mu U/T$

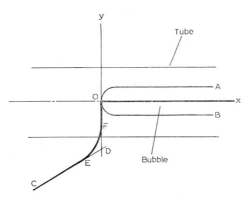

Fig. 1. Distribution of pressure in a tube due to a bubble.

is small, a knowledge of F_2 is not nearly so important as that of F_1 in most cases unless $\mu U/T$ is small.

The problem presented by a bubble in a capillary tube was considered first because it is the simplest definable and easiest realizable case of separation in a viscous fluid when the Reynolds number is so small that only the balance of viscous stresses and surface tension need be taken into account. The analogous problem where a two-dimensional bubble is forced into fluid contained between two parallel plates cannot be materialized because the meniscus is unstable (SAFFMAN AND TAYLOR[3], 1958) though cases with more complicated geometry, such as the flow when a cylinder rolls on a plane covered with viscous fluid, may involve a stable meniscus. There is, however, no reason why the unstable equilibrium configuration should not be calculated.

FLOW IN A NARROW GAP BETWEEN ECCENTRIC ROTATING CYLINDERS

The flow in a long, fully lubricated bearing is well understood. To avoid geometrical complexities, the simplest case will be considered; namely, that of a very eccentric bearing or more definitely the narrow space or nip where two cylinders nearly come into contact, and the equations for the flow in that region will be reproduced in order to develop a method for finding where the meniscus could be located. The physical properties of the meniscus will be assumed to be analogous to those of the bubble in a capillary tube; namely, that at the meniscus,

$$m = F_1(\mu U/T) \tag{3}$$

and

$$-\delta p = \frac{\mu U}{h} F_2(\mu U/T). \tag{4}$$

Here m is the ratio of the amount of fluid flowing at any section to the amount which would flow if the pressure gradient there were zero, and h is the distance between the surfaces. Two cases may be considered: (a) both surfaces are moving with velocity U, then $m = q/Uh$ where q is the volume flowing past the nip per unit length, and (b) only one surface is moving, as in the case of a bearing, then $m = 2q/Uh$.

If x is the distance along the nip measured from the narrowest point where $h = h_0$, the variation of h with x can be expressed by the equation

$$h = h_0 + x^2/2R \tag{5}$$

Here

$$R = (R_1^{-1} - R_2^{-1})^{-1} \tag{6}$$

where R_1 and R_2 are the radii of the cylinders, R_2 being the larger, and R_1 and R_2 are taken as both positive if the centre of R_1 is within R_2. When the case considered is that of a cylinder rolling on a plane, R is evidently the radius of that cylinder.

It is convenient to use a co-ordinate θ, instead of x, defined by

$$\tan \theta = x(2Rh_0)^{-1/2}. \tag{7}$$

The equation for the distribution of pressure according to Reynolds' approximation then takes the non-dimensional form

$$\frac{dp'}{d\theta} = \cos^2 \theta - \lambda \cos^4 \theta. \tag{8}$$

This equation applies to both cases (a) and (b), but in case (a) the pressure p is related to p' by

$$p = p'\{12\mu U (2R)^{1/2}h_0^{-3/2}\} \tag{9a}$$

and in case (b)

$$p = \tfrac{1}{2}p'\{12\mu U (2R)^{1/2}h_0^{-3/2}\}. \tag{9b}$$

References p. 101

In both cases (a) and (b), λ is the ratio of the total flow through the nip to the flow if there had been no pressure gradient at $\theta = 0$, so that in both cases (a) and (b)

$$\lambda h_0 = mh. \tag{10}$$

The solution of (8) is

$$p' = \tfrac{1}{2}\theta + \tfrac{1}{4}\pi + \tfrac{1}{4}\sin 2\theta - \lambda\left[\tfrac{3}{8}\theta + \tfrac{3}{16}\pi + \tfrac{1}{4}\sin 2\theta + \tfrac{1}{32}\sin 4\theta\right] \tag{11}$$

where the constant of integration has been chosen so that $p' = 0$ when $\theta = -\pi/2$, i.e., the pressure is atmospheric far from the nip in the upstream direction.

When $\lambda = 4/3$, $p = 0$ at $\theta = +\pi/2$ as well as at $\theta = -\pi/2$, and the distribution of p' is antisymmetrical, being positive when $\theta < 0$ and negative when $\theta > 0$. The distribution of p' in this case is shown in Fig. 2.

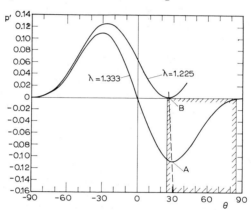

Fig. 2. Distribution of pressure (a) when completely flooded and (b) when the Swift-Stieber condition is satisfied at B.

POSITION OF MENISCUS

To find the position of the meniscus for given values of $\mu U/T$ and h_0/R, a diagram like Fig. 2 may be used. Lines showing the variation of p' with θ for constant λ can be plotted, but it is not necessary to cover the whole field because, as has been noted many times in the literature of lubrication theory, the flow can divide in a place only when $\mathrm{d}p/\mathrm{d}x$ is positive. Fig. 3 which covers a part of the field where a meniscus could occur has, therefore, been prepared using the expression (11) and calculating p' for given values of θ and λ.

The diagram of Fig. 3 is particularly suitable for finding the locus of the points where condition (3) can be satisfied for both case (a) and case (b). The definition of m as the ratio of the amount of fluid passing through the nip to the amount which would flow if there were no pressure gradient leads to

$$m = \lambda h_0/h = \lambda \cos^2 \theta. \tag{12}$$

Thus lines of constant m can be drawn and according to eqn. (3) these will be lines of constant $\mu U/T$. Such lines are shown in the figure for values of m from 0.03 to 0.55 and for $m = 1$. Evidently $m = 1$ is the line which represents the point where, if it were possible, the flow could divide without changing velocity; that is, it is the line $dp'/d\theta = 0$, or, using (12), $\cos^2 \theta = \lambda^{-1}$.

To fix the point in Fig. 3 which represents the meniscus, it is necessary to know

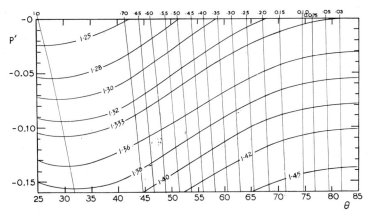

Fig. 3. Contours of p' for constant values of λ (1.25 to 1.45), and of m (0.03 to 0.70 and also 1.0).

h_0 as well as $\mu U/T$. Assuming that we have measured $F_2(\mu U/T)$, the corresponding values of p' using (4) and (9) are

$$-p' = \tfrac{1}{12} \left(\frac{h_0}{2R} \right)^{1/2} F_2 \left(\frac{\mu U}{T} \right) \cos^2 \theta \quad \text{in case (a)} \tag{13a}$$

$$-p' = \tfrac{1}{6} \left(\frac{h_0}{2R} \right)^{1/2} F_2 \left(\frac{\mu U}{T} \right) \cos^2 \theta \quad \text{in case (b)} \tag{13b}$$

If F_2 were measured experimentally or calculated as a function of $\mu U/T$, eqn. (13) would be used to superpose lines of constant h_0/R on Fig. 3; and the intersections of these lines with those of constant m, and therefore constant $\mu U/T$, would determine the points at which the meniscus would lie for any given value of $\mu U/T$ and h_0/R. It will be noticed that when h_0/R is very small, as it is in most bearings, p' is also small and the position of the meniscus is determined simply by the point where the axis $p' = 0$ cuts the appropriate line of constant $\mu U/T$, unless $F_2(\mu U/T)$ is very large. In other words, it is necessary to know only $F_1(\mu U/T)$ in such cases.

MEASUREMENT OF $F_1(\mu U/T)$. APPARATUS

The main difficulty in measuring m' is to obtain two-dimensional flow because the meniscus is unstable when the two surfaces are parallel. It is true that the meniscus may be stable in the diverging region downstream of the nip, but the conditions which lead to such stability are not well understood. Another difficulty

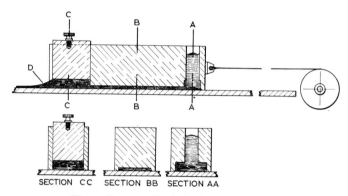

Fig. 4. Perspex (Lucite) block apparatus.

is that of measuring m in a journal bearing. To collect and measure q, the volume which passes the nip per second, would be very difficult. In designing apparatus for determining m as a function of $\mu U/T$, it seemed best to attempt to control m and measure U. If the meniscus had been stable, this would perhaps have involved varying U till the meniscus was brought to rest, but the instability prevented the direct use of this method. It was found, however, that the configuration illustrated in Fig. 4 stabilized the meniscus at slow speeds.

A perspex (Lucite R) block was cut accurately rectangular and a very uniform trough 0.05 cm deep and 12.4 cm long was cut in its lower face. This trough did not extend to the front end of the block. The apparatus could slide on a piece of plate glass, selected optically for flatness, and as it moved it deposited a sheet of fluid 0.025 cm thick on the glass. The fluid was supplied at a vertical chamber cut in the perspex as indicated at the section AA in Fig. 4. The object of the long shallow trough was merely to regulate the supply of fluid to an observation chamber between the glass and a second short adjustable block of perspex, which is shown in the section CC. This block was 4.5 cm long. If h_0 is the depth of the regulating trough and h_1 the height of the channel beneath the movable block, the flow in this chamber can be defined by the ratio

$$m = \frac{\text{actual flow in observation chamber}}{\text{flow which would exist if there were no pressure gradient there}}$$

If the regulating trough were very long, the flow in it would be simply $\frac{1}{2}Uh_0$ where U is the velocity of the block over the glass. Therefore, the actual flow in the chamber at C is $\frac{1}{2}Uh_0$, but if there were no pressure gradient in the observation chamber the flow would be $\frac{1}{2}Uh_1$ so that

$$m = h_0/h_1. \tag{14}$$

Owing to the fact that the length C of the observation chamber was small compared with that of the regulating space, it was first considered justifiable to take m as h_0/h_1, but later a correction was applied.

The experiment consisted in towing the block in a straight line over the glass at gradually increasing speeds till the meniscus, shown at D in Fig. 4, began to move forward into the observation chamber, C. It was always found that the meniscus was unstable when it began to penetrate the chamber. Fingers of air formed and always ran forward as far as the end of the regulating space. As the speed increased the meniscus became more and more hollow till it appeared to become tangential to the horizontal lower surface of the movable block just before it began to penetrate the observation chamber.

The measured value of U was multiplied by the factor μ/T and m plotted against $\mu U/T$. Some points in Fig. 6 were obtained in this way.

It was noticed in these experiments that the meniscus was usually curved in the horizontal plane before it developed instability. This was likely to be a source of error which could have been reduced by using a wider block. It was also found that at the higher speeds the steady conditions hardly had time to be established before the block reached the end of its travel, which was limited to 30 inches, the length of the glass.

CYLINDRICAL APPARATUS

To overcome these difficulties, a new apparatus was designed in which a cylinder could rotate continuously in a trough of fluid, and a fixed concentric arc with clearance h_0 was used to regulate the flow into an observation chamber. This apparatus is shown in the sketch, Fig. 5. A cylinder B of radius 7.60 cm and length 38.0 cm could rotate in ball bearings held in a strong steel frame. A regulating perspex block A whose lower surface was a cylinder of radius 7.65 cm, was fixed concentric with the cylinder so that the regulating space between them was 0.05 cm thick. The angle covered by this block was 78°* so that the length of the regulating space was 10.4 cm. The width in the direction of the generators of the cylinder was 22.4 cm. The accuracy of the setting was ensured by laying flexible spacers 0.050 cm thick on the cylinder and then bringing the regulating block

---

* The exact measurement had been mislaid when Fig. 5 was drawn. The value 78° was measured later when the apparatus was dismantled.

onto them. In this position the block was fixed to a strong frame by suitable adjusting screws. The fluid was contained in a trough C (Fig. 5) which was filled up to the level of the top of the cylinder. Leakage at the point where the $\frac{1}{2}''$ steel axle of the cylinder passed through the ends of the trough C was prevented by means of O-rings set in the steel frame. The trough, which was made of tinned steel sheet, was slightly flexible so that as the trough filled a small leak began to develop as the weight of fluid increased during filling. This was cured by adjusting supports between the strong frame and the trough.

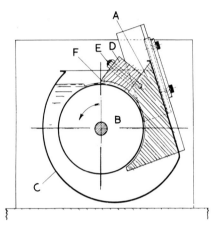

Fig. 5. Cylindrical apparatus.

The observation chamber in which the meniscus was observed was the space under a perspex block D (Fig. 5) which was fixed by bolts E passing through slots in D. This construction allowed for adjustment of the distance h_1 of D from the cylinder. The bottom of the block D was a part of a cylinder with a radius of 7.65 cm. To set up the apparatus flexible sheets of the required thickness were made and placed on the cylinder. The block D was then laid so that its rear face was in contact with the forward face of the regulating block (which was in an axial plane), and its forward bottom corner F was in contact with the flexible spacers. Since the spacers were lying on the cylinder and the block covered an angle of 36°, the thickness of the observation chamber was slightly greater at the rear than at the forward end by an amount $(h_1 - h_0)$ (sec 36° − 1). The cylinder was driven through continuously varying and fixed reduction gears by a constant speed motor so that the peripheral velocity U of the cylinder could be slowly increased till the meniscus withdrew from the forward end, F, of the observation chamber. As with the perspex slider shown in Fig. 4, the cavitating air-fingers always ran back to the rear end of the observation chamber. The speed U at which this occurred could be determined with good repeatability, but to ensure

References p. 101

that the flow was two-dimensional it was necessary to fit end plates lined with sorbo-rubber or felt which could be fitted to the end of regulating block A and to D to prevent air or fluid from being sucked laterally into the rear end of the observation chamber where the lowest pressure occurred. Even this precaution had to be supplemented by guide vanes outside the end plates to ensure that the outside of the felt or sorbo-rubber lining was flooded with the fluid. It was found that if any air got through, bubbles in the observation chamber destroyed the two-dimensional character of the flow and upset the conditions leading to the instability of the meniscus.

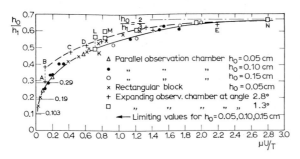

Fig. 6. Measurements of $\mu U/T$ at which flow ceased to be two-dimensional for fixed values of h_0/h_1.

The fluids used were pure glycerine and glycerine diluted with 5 per cent water. The viscosity of the fluid used was measured at a range of temperatures and the temperature was measured before and after each experiment. Glycerine does not wet perspex completely and a thin sheet of glycerine on the surface develops dry areas after a time. This fact does not seem to affect the critical value of U, for in the perspex block experiments both wetting oils and glycerine were used and no difference was found between the results obtained. Oil was not used in the cylinder apparatus because of the difficulty of cleaning it. The surface tension T was taken as 63 dyn/cm throughout because the variation with temperature was small. Some uncorrected results obtained with the regulating chamber of uniform depth, $h_0 = 0.05$ cm, are marked in Fig. 6 by the symbol △. It will be seen that these are in fairly good agreement with those obtained with the flat perspex block, at any rate up to $\mu U/T = 0.6$. At higher values of $\mu U/T$, the limitations of the flat block apparatus made the results unreliable.

EXPERIMENTS WITH LARGER REGULATING CHANNEL

As the speed rose the difficulty of excluding bubbles from the chamber increased and the highest value of $\mu U/T$ obtainable was 0.6. To increase $\mu U/T$ without increasing the suction at the rear end of the observation chamber, it was necessary to increase h_0. To make a regulating space uniform with thickness 0.1 cm, the cylindrical surface of the block A (Fig. 5) should have been re-machined to a radius 7.70, and in fact this has now been done, but the experiments have not yet been repeated with the re-machined block. On the other hand, the flow regulating effect of a long narrow space upstream of the observation chamber does not depend on its having a uniform thickness, but a correction must be applied when it does not.

CORRECTIONS

If h is known as a function of x, the distance along the regulating block, the equivalent thickness of the block of the same length but uniform thickness which would deliver the same volume per second can be found by integrating Reynolds' equation. If q is the volumetric rate of flow per cm of the meniscus, Reynolds' approximation is

$$\frac{1}{12\mu}\frac{\mathrm{d}p}{\mathrm{d}x} = \frac{U}{h^2} - \frac{q}{h^3} \qquad \text{in case (a)} \qquad (15a)$$

$$\frac{1}{12\mu}\frac{\mathrm{d}p}{\mathrm{d}x} = \frac{U}{2h^2} - \frac{q}{h^3} \qquad \text{in case (b).} \qquad (15b)$$

When h is uniform and there is no pressure gradient $h = 2q/U$ in case (b), and if h is variable but there is no difference in pressure at the two ends of the channel

$$q \int \frac{\mathrm{d}x}{h^3} = \tfrac{1}{2} U \int \frac{\mathrm{d}x}{h^2} \qquad (16)$$

the integrals extending along the block. Hence

$$m = \frac{2q}{h_1 U} = \frac{\displaystyle\int h^{-2}\,\mathrm{d}x}{h_1 \displaystyle\int h^{-3}\,\mathrm{d}x} \qquad (17)$$

the integrals extending the total length of the regulating and observation chambers, but it is convenient to express (17) non-dimensionally in the form

$$m = \frac{h_0}{h_1} \cdot \frac{\displaystyle\int \left(\frac{h_0}{h}\right)^2 \mathrm{d}x}{\displaystyle\int \left(\frac{h_0}{h}\right)^3 \mathrm{d}x} \qquad (18)$$

where h_0 is to be taken as some easily measurable quantity.

References p. 101

To set the regulating block so that it formed a channel which was wider than 0.05 cm, flexible spacers 0.10 cm thick were laid on the cylinder and the perspex block of radius 7.65 cm was brought down onto them and fixed rigidly. The depth of the channel at all points of the regulating space has first to be found. At its two ends it is h_0 ($= 0.1$ cm in the present case). If the radius of the lower surface of the regulating block is $R + \delta$, R being the radius of the cylinder and δ being in the present case 0.050 cm, then the depth h of the regulating space can be found by remembering that the method of setting up the regulating block ensures that h is symmetrical about its mid-point. If ϕ is the angular co-ordinate and the mid-point of the regulating space is $\phi = 0$, it is found that

$$h = h_0 \{\alpha + (1 - \alpha) \sec \phi_0 \cos \phi\} \tag{19}$$

where $\alpha = \delta/h_0$. To apply (19) it is sufficiently accurate to take the depth in the observation chamber as uniform and equal to h_1, which is the measured depth of the channel at the forward end F (Fig. 5). The contributions of the observation chamber to the integrals in (18) are then $(h_0/h_1)^2\phi_2$ and $(h_0/h_1)^3\phi_2$ to the numerator and denominator, respectively, where ϕ_2 is the angle covered by the observation chamber, in the present case $\phi_2 = 36°$. If $2\phi_0$ is the angle subtended by the regulating block (in this case 78°), the expression for m is therefore

$$m = \frac{h_0}{h_1} \cdot \frac{\left(\dfrac{h_0}{h_1}\right)^2 \phi_2 + \displaystyle\int_{-\phi_0}^{+\phi_2} \{\alpha + (1 - \alpha) \sec \phi_0 \cos \phi\}^{-2} \, d\phi}{\left(\dfrac{h_0}{h_1}\right)^3 \phi_2 + \displaystyle\int_{-\phi_0}^{+\phi_0} \{\alpha + (1 - \alpha) \sec \phi_0 \cos \phi\}^{-3} \, d\phi}. \tag{20}$$

For the case when $\delta = h_0 = 0.05$ cm, $\alpha = 1$ and (20) reduces to

$$m \frac{h_1}{h_0} = K_{0.05} = \frac{\left(\dfrac{h_0}{h_1}\right)^2 + \dfrac{78}{36}}{\left(\dfrac{h_0}{h_1}\right)^3 + \dfrac{78}{36}} \tag{21}$$

where $K_{0.05}$ is a correcting factor to be applied to the approximation (14). The correcting factor K_{block} for the perspex block, which had a regulating channel 12.4 cm long and an observation chamber 4.5 cm long, is the same as (21) except that 78/30 is replaced by 12.4/4.5. The calculated values of $K_{0.1}$, $K_{0.05}$, and K_{block} are given in Table I. The value of $K_{0.1}$ was calculated by numerical integration from (20).

References p. 101

TABLE I

CORRECTION FACTORS TO BE APPLIED TO MEASURED h_0/h_1

h_0/h_1	0.1	0.2	0.3	0.4	0.5	0.6	0.7	0.8
$K_{0.1}$	1.095	1.108	1.125	1.142	1.153	1.156	1.147	1.122
$K_{0.05}$	1.004	1.015	1.029	1.043	1.055	1.060	1.058	1.048
K_{block}	1.006	1.010	1.020	1.035	1.046	1.047	1.050	1.040

EFFECT OF GRAVITY

The neglect of the effect of gravity at the meniscus produces little error except at very slow speeds. There is a limiting value of h above which the meniscus will leave the leading edge of the observation chamber no matter how small U may be. Since the thickness of the fluid sheet which is carried away is $\frac{1}{2}h_0$, the height of the bottom of the observation chamber above the top of the sheet is $h - \frac{1}{2}h_0$ and the hydrostatic force, which must be balanced by surface tension force, LT, is $\frac{1}{2}g\varrho(h - \frac{1}{2}h_0)^2$. Thus the minimum value of m when $U = 0$ is

$$\frac{\digamma h_0}{\dfrac{h_0}{2} + \dfrac{4T}{g}}$$

For glycerine $4T/g = 0.46$ cm so that the value of m at $U = 0$ is $h_0/(\frac{1}{2}h_0 + 0.46)$. When h_0 is 0.05 this is $m = 0.103$, for $h_0 = 0.1$ it is $m = 0.195$, and for $h_0 = 0.155$ it is $m = 0.29$. These limits are marked on Fig. 6. At first sight one might be inclined to think that since the value of m at $U = 0$ is comparable with that at finite values of $\mu U/T$, large errors might arise owing to the effect of gravity. This, however, seems to me unlikely because as soon as U is finite, a comparatively large pressure defect at the meniscus can be built up by a very small change in the flow through the regulating channel; all that gravity does it to change very slightly the rate of flow which is necessary to set up the conditions at the meniscus which lead to its retreat into the observation chamber. The values of m deduced by applying the correcting factors of Table I are shown in Fig. 7.

The principal generalizations that these experiments suggest are:

(1) The value of m at which the meniscus begins to retreat into the channel is a function of $\mu U/T$ only.

(2) As $\mu U/T$ increases, m appears to approach an asymptotic value which is above, but not far from, $\frac{2}{3}$, which is the value it has when the flow close to the fixed surface begins to reverse its direction at points in the chamber, where the effect of the meniscus in deflecting the stream lines is negligible and the Reynolds approximation holds.

(3) At small values of $\mu U/T$, the curve gives the impression of being parabolic.

A similar approximation has been noted in the case of a bubble in a capillary tube (FAIRBROTHER AND STUBBS[4], 1935, and TAYLOR[1], 1961) though it has been shown (BRETHERTON[5], 1961) that the approximation ceases to be valid when m is less than about 10^{-3}. A rough approximation for the parabolic range of Fig. 7 is $m = 0.85\ (\mu U/T)^{\frac{1}{2}}$. Fairbrother and Stubbs' empirical formula was $m = 1.0\ (\mu U/T)^{\frac{1}{2}}$, but there is no reason to expect exact agreement between the two expressions.

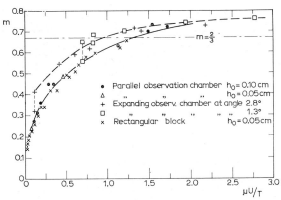

Fig. 7. Values of m corrected from Table I.

EXPERIMENTS WITH DIVERGING OBSERVATION CHAMBER

The fact that the meniscus does not seem to be able to travel back when m is greater than some number, which is in the neighborhood of $\frac{2}{3}$, suggests that if the observation channel were made to diverge instead of being parallel—so that m could vary through the observation chamber from some small number to 1.0—the air cavity would not be able to reach the regulating block but would stop at some intermediate point. To make the observation chamber diverge, some thin perspex wedges were cut and placed base downwards between the blocks A and D (Fig. 5). These were able to give the chamber divergence angles of 1.3° and 2.8°, respectively. They were set with bases at the level of the top of the regulating space so that the maximum value of h_0/h was 1.0, at the upstream end of the observation channel. As U was gradually increased, the meniscus became unstable at the same value of $\mu U/T$ as when the channel was parallel and with the same value of h at the open end. The instability which then occurred was very similar to that observed when air is forced into fluid contained between parallel plates (SAFFMAN AND TAYLOR[3], 1958). It developed into air fingers which were separated by fluid columns whose widths were comparable with that of the fingers. Fig. 8 is a photograph of the meniscus at that stage using the narrow wedge which made the chamber

References p. 101

diverge at 1.3°. The fingers remained in this condition as long as the speed was kept constant (in fact, the exposure of this photograph was 8 seconds) and their ends remained roughly on a generator of the cylinder corresponding with a constant value of h. In this photograph and all those that follow, the inner cylinders or journals rotated about their horizontal axes in such a direction that the near sides were always moving upward. In every case the outer cylinder, or perspex block, was stationary.

Fig. 8. Air fingers corresponding with $\mu U/T = 0.11$, $h_0 = 0.05$ cm, divergence 1.3°.

The depth of the observation chamber at the level of the ends of the fingers was measured by inserting strips of flexible plastic material (polythene) of known thickness as feelers. The results of these measurements are shown in Figs. 6 and 7 by means of crosses $+$ in the case of the wider divergence, 2.8°, of the observation chamber, and by squares $\square$ for the smaller divergence, 1.3°. The lower left cross and square represent the values of h_0/h where the meniscus began to retreat from the forward edge of the observation chamber. Within the accuracy of the measurements, they lie on the curve obtained using the nearly parallel but very slightly *converging* channel obtained by bolting the movable block D (Fig. 5) directly to the regulating block A without inserting the wedges. The cross and square directly above these (Figs. 6 and 7) represent the points to which the meniscus retracted keeping the speed constant. The photograph of Fig. 8 corresponds with this latter square, but as will be seen this point was not very well determined since the ends of the fingers did not all come to rest at the same value of h.

As the speed increased the fingers moved inwards so that h decreased and $m = h_0/h$ increased. Their number also increased and the widths of the fluid

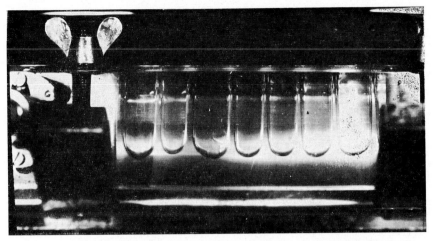

Fig. 9. Air fingers corresponding with $\mu U/T = 1.3$, $h_0 = 0.05$ cm, divergence 2.8°.

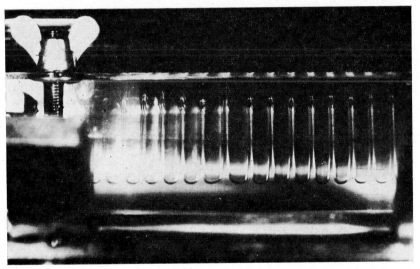

Fig. 10. Air fingers corresponding with $\mu U/T = 4.0$, $h_0 = 0.05$ cm, divergence 2.8°.

streams separating them decreased. Fig. 9 shows the condition when the divergence is 2.8° and $\mu U/T = 1.3$. Fig. 10 shows the condition at the divergence 2.8° and $\mu U/T = 4$. It will be noticed that except for the case when the meniscus first leaves the stabilizing edge of the adjustable block, the ends of the fingers lie remarkably closely on a line of constant h and that as the speed increases, this line, whose movement is represented by the dotted curve in Figs. 6 and 7, seems to approach more and more closely to the same asymptote as that of the two-

References p. 101

dimensional or cylindrical meniscus which is about to become unstable. Thus the asymptotic condition for large $\mu U/T$ seems to be one in which the flow separates, so that the most of the fluid which leaves the region of separation is carried away on the cylinder in a sheet of uniform thickness and only a very little is carried in the form of the thin sheets perpendicular to the cylinder which separate the air fingers. This point is referred to later and is strikingly verified in Fig. 14.

CAVITATION

The separation just described necessarily involves a pressure gradient upstream of the meniscus which leads to pressures so low that true cavitation must occur. BANKS AND MILL[6] (1954), for instance, experimenting with apparatus in which both cylinders moved (case a), showed photographs of cavitating bubbles appearing at the point of lowest pressure in the flooded nip between two rotating cylinders. At speeds where the cavitation pressure is just attained at the point of minimum pressure, these bubbles will not grow. They may disappear or they may be carried round as small bubbles. When the speed is higher so that the cavitation pressure extends over a larger area, the bubbles will grow and will alter the pressure in the fluid round them. Finally they become continuous and form fingers or streaks of air which carry the atmosphere pressure upstream. This seems to be the condition visualized by SWIFT[7] in the asymptotic case where $\mu U/T$ is large. Curve (a), Fig. 2, shows the non-dimensional pressure curve for a flooded nip for which $\lambda = \frac{4}{3}$. Bubbles will appear first at the point A. As the bubble spreads the minimum pressure will be reduced, and λ will therefore also be reduced. This process can proceed till the bubbles extend to the atmosphere and the pressure at the level of their vertices is atmospheric. The point B is then reached on the curve $\lambda = 1.225$, where $p = 0$ and $\mathrm{d}p/\mathrm{d}x = 0$. The fingers of air cannot penetrate further because that would involve separation in the part of the pressure curve where $\mathrm{d}p/\mathrm{d}x$ is positive, which is impossible. The point B, Fig. 2, represents Swift's condition in the case of a very eccentric bearing.

The shapes of the air fingers in Swift's type of cavitation must depend on two independent causes, both of which tend to make the flooded areas between them get narrower downstream. One cause is geometrical and is due to the widening of the gap h, while the other is the transfer of fluid beneath the meniscus. The points of the air fingers may be expected to be paraboloidal while they are still narrower than h, since that is the axisymmetrical shape whose cross section increases linearly. This paraboloidal part would only extend to a length comparable with h and thereafter the shape will be determined by the two causes. If only the first cause were operative, flooded areas between the fingers would occupy a proportion, h/h_s, of the whole, h_s being the value of h at the points of the fingers.

References p. 101

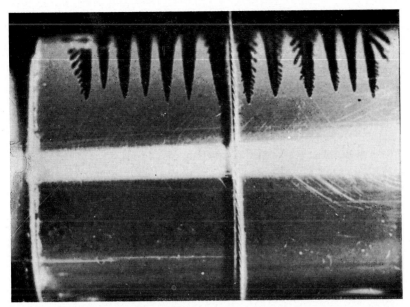

Fig. 11. Cavitation between shaft and transparent bush at $\mu U/T \sim 0.12$, $h_0 \sim 1.0 \times 10^{-3}$ cm.

Fig. 12. Cavitation between shaft and transparent bush at $\mu U/T \sim 0.03$, $h_0 \sim 0.3 \times 10^{-3}$ cm.

In that case the air spaces would not join together. The second cause would make the flooded areas get narrower more rapidly than would be expected from purely geometrical considerations.

These speculations resulted from a study of some photographs sent to me by Prof. J. A. Cole. They show the cavitation of oil through a loaded perspex bush on a rotating shaft. Fig. 11 shows the air fingers (black) when the shaft, 0.9820 inches in diameter, is rotating at 138 revs/min in a bush 0.9840 inches in diameter and 1.63 inches long. Fig. 12 shows the same bearing with the same load, the shaft rotating at 34.6 revs/min. It was not possible to measure h, but it is clear that it must have been greater at 138 than at 34 revs. This may account for the greater distance between the fingers in Fig. 11 compared with Fig. 12. If the geometrical cause for the narrowing of the oil streaks were the only one operating, it would have been expected that reduction in their width at a given distance from the beginning of cavitation would be less in Fig. 11 than in Fig. 12. The fact that this is not true shows that the second cause; namely, the transfer of fluid across the meniscus, is operative and is probably the principal cause of the much wider angle of the pointed end of the air finger in Fig. 11 than in Fig. 12.

COMPARISON OF TWO TYPES OF CAVITATION OR SEPARATION

Comparison of Figs. 11 and 12 with Figs. 9 and 10 reveals the physical difference between the two types. In separation the motion is mainly two-dimensional. The thin partitions between the air fingers carry only a small part of the fluid, the rest is carried in a thin sheet of uniform thickness on the moving surface. In true cavitation, starting inside the fluid, much of it is carried in columns filling the space between the two surfaces and separated by air fingers. In bearings these columns may be carried round the shaft unbroken or they may break down leaving a sheet of lubricant of variable thickness on the shaft. When this happens the meniscus, which is the boundary of the region where the oil film is reformed on the far side of the bearing, may be expected to reproduce approximately the pattern of the fingers formed in the cavitation region. Fig. 13 is one of Prof. Cole's photographs showing the reformation of the oil film under conditions where widely separated air fingers were formed in the location of the true cavitation. Sometimes, however, Prof. Cole obtained quite a different kind of reformation meniscus. Fig. 14 is an example. In that case both the speed and the load were each $\frac{1}{8}$th of that used in the experiment for Fig. 12 so that the eccentricity, and therefore the geometry, in the two cases should be nearly identical. On the other hand, both the maximum negative pressure which would exist if the film were continuous and $\mu U/T$ were only $\frac{1}{8}$th of that appropriate to Fig. 12. It is, therefore, to be expected that true cavitation would be more likely to occur under the conditions of Fig. 14

References p. 101

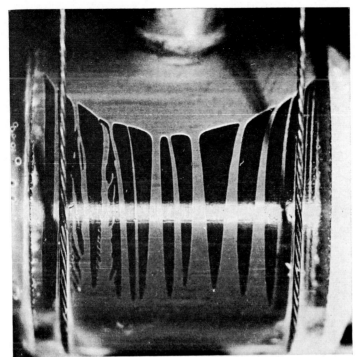

Fig. 13. Photograph showing both the formation of air fingers and the reformation of the oil film.

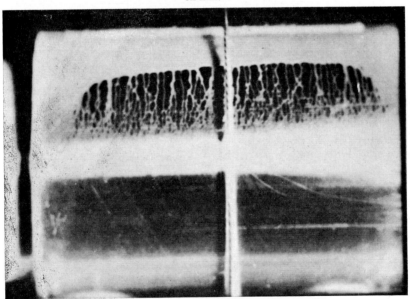

Fig. 14. Photograph showing the reformation of the oil film for the same geometry as in Fig. 13 but with $\mu U/T \sim 0.004$.

References p. 101

than those of Fig. 12. Unfortunately the illumination failed to show the part of the bearing where cavitation began in Fig. 14, but the fact that the re-forming meniscus is smooth suggests that the layer of oil carried round on the shaft was of uniform thickness. The thin lines seen in the cavitated area can only represent a small proportion of the oil carried round and may well be the remains of the thin films which separate the air fingers produced by separation rather than true cavitation.

Since writing this paper Prof. Birkhoff called my attention to a number of papers by FLOBERG[8],[9] [See Floberg's paper in these proceedings (p. 138)]. In one of them[8], he shows photographs very like Prof. Cole's. In another[9], he shows photographs of cavitation of heavy Vactric lubricating oil when a cylinder, 8 cm

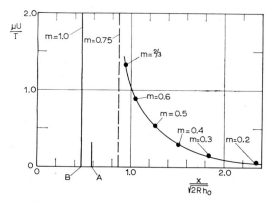

Fig. 15. Values for which both sorts of cavitation might be expected in Floberg's experiments.

in diameter and 8 cm long, was rotated at distance $h_0 = 0.01, 0.02, 0.04,$ and 0.06 cm. These were very like mine except that they are much better photographs, but those at $h_0 = 0.01$ cm are quite unlike mine. Possibly the former show separation and the latter cavitation.

Floberg did not give any indication of the viscosity of the oil he used except to give its trade name, nor did his photographs show the position of the nip—the point where the two surfaces were closest together—so that I cannot compare them with the ideas put forward here. Floberg does point out that, except in the case of his smallest gap, the ends of the air fingers were further from the nip than would be calculated using Swift's condition. For $m = \frac{2}{3}$ the distances of the cavitation fingers from the nip would be larger for the separation condition than the Swift condition in the ratio

$$\frac{\tan 43.2°}{\tan 25.4°} = 1.98.$$

References p. 101

Floberg calls attention to the fact that as the speed decreased his cavitation fingers retreated from the nip. This is what would be expected for separation-cavitation but not for vapor pressure-cavitation.

To make comparisons between theory and experiment, I have constructed the curve, Fig. 15, which shows the values of $x/\sqrt{2Rh_0}$ at which the two sorts of cavitation might be expected in Floberg's experiments if the space upstream of the nip were flooded. Here A is the minimum pressure point when there is no cavitation and the whole space is flooded; B is the Swift point. The curve shows the outer range of the points at which separation-cavitation might establish itself, *i.e.*, it corresponds with the full line in Fig. 7. The broken line in Fig. 7 is not well enough established by my experiments to use, but if it were, the corresponding curve in Fig. 15 would have the same asymptote as that shown, corresponding with $m = 0.75$, and would lie a little below it.

REFERENCES

1 G. I. TAYLOR, *J. Fluid Mech.*, 10 (1961) 161.
2 B. G. COX, *J. Fluid Mech.*, 14 (1962) 81–96.
3 P. G. SAFFMAN AND G. I. TAYLOR, The Penetration of a Fluid into a Porous Medium or Hele-Shaw Cell Containing a More Viscous Liquid, *Proc. Roy. Soc. (London)*, A245 (1958).
4 F. FAIRBROTHER AND A. E. STUBBS, *J. Chem. Soc.*, 1 (1935) 527.
5 F. P. BRETHERTON, *J. Fluid Mech.*, 10 (1961) 166.
6 W. H. BANKS AND C. C. MILL, Some Observations on the Behavior of Liquids Between Rotating Cylinders, *Proc. Roy. Soc. (London)*, A223 (1954).
7 H. W. SWIFT, *Proc. Inst. Civil Engrs. (London)*, 1932, p. 233.
8 L. FLOBERG, Experimental Investigation of Cavitation Regions in Journal Bearings, *Trans. Chalmers Univ. Technol. (Gothenburg)*, No. 238, 1961.
9 L. FLOBERG, Lubrication of Two Cylindrical Surfaces, Considering Cavitation, *Trans. Chalmers Univ. Technol. (Gothenburg)*, No. 234, 1961.

Free Boundary Problems for Viscous Flows in Channels

GARRETT BIRKHOFF*

Department of Mathematics, Harvard University, Cambridge, Massachusetts

I. INTRODUCTION

SIR GEOFFREY TAYLOR (p. 80) has discussed two interesting physical phenomena: the longitudinal penetration by air of a cylindrical tube filled with a viscous fluid, and the cavitation and flow separation which occurs in lubricating films between two rotating cylinders. Most of my talk will be devoted to discussing these phenomena from a mathematical standpoint.

To a mathematician, the problem is to formulate precisely and solve boundary value problems, whose variables are supposed to represent the quantities of greatest physical interest. Typically, this means finding physically reasonable differential equations and boundary conditions, from which the solution can be calculated by purely mathematical arguments. A good mathematician will not consider the formulation satisfactory unless the boundary value problem is *well-set*—that is, unless the differential equations assumed have one and only one solution for the given boundary values, and unless this solution depends continuously on these values.

I will first consider from this mathematical standpoint the simpler of the two preceding problems: cavitation and flow separation in viscous films between adjacent rotating cylinders. To be specific, I will suppose that the two cylinders have peripheral velocities $U = r_1\omega_1$ and $V = r_2\omega_2$, respectively (see Fig. 1). Special cases include a cylindrical slider, two rollers, and a cylindrical journal bearing.

The generally accepted differential equation of this problem was found by OSBORNE REYNOLDS[9]. If $h(x)$ denotes the clearance width, and $p(x)$ the pressure in the oil film in the clearance space then (Ref. 7, p. 11), assuming incompressibility,

$$\mathrm{d}(h^3\mathrm{d}p/\mu\mathrm{d}x)/\mathrm{d}x = 6(U+V)\mathrm{d}h/\mathrm{d}x. \tag{1}$$

---

* Work partly supported by the Office of Naval Research.

References p. 120–121

In a journal bearing, and indeed generally, it is natural to impose the boundary condition of *periodicity*: the net change $\oint dp$ in pressure around the cylinder is zero. This defines a boundary value problem which is well-set, in the sense of having a solution for given $h(x)$ which is unique up to an additive constant. Since the net thrust (integrated vector pressure) is independent of this constant, the theory is mathematically satisfactory.

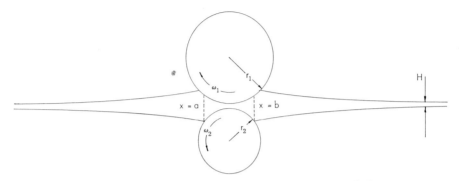

Fig. 1. Flow separation from adjacent counter-rotating cylinders.

But in heavily loaded journal bearings, underpressures arise in the divergent region (Ref. 7, p. 46), and these violate the first boundary condition of cavitation theory (Ref. 1, p. 7):

$$p = p_v \quad \text{on the boundary}$$
$$p \geq p_v \quad \text{in the liquid phase} \tag{2a}$$

(p_v = vapor pressure; in practical lubrication problems, one can set $p_v = 0$.) Likewise, if air has access to the ends of the oil film, one naturally assumes the analogous condition involving atmospheric pressure p_a:

$$p = p_a \quad \text{on the liquid-air interface.} \tag{2b}$$

This gives rise to the following *free boundary problem*: using (1) and (2a) or (2b), how can one predict the pressure distribution in a cavitating or separating film, and the extent of this film?

I will discuss this problem in sections 2–4 below; the discussion will mainly summarize recent joint research with D. F. HAYS[15]. I will then consider, in sections 5–6, the related problem of the growth of a cavity in a Hele-Shaw cell. This is the plane analog of the problem of a 'finger' of non-viscous fluid penetrating a tube discussed by Sir Geoffrey Taylor.

References p. 120–121

A. HYDRODYNAMIC PARTIAL LUBRICATION

2. GENERAL DISCUSSION

Before studying the special free boundary problem formulated in section 1, I should like to recall some relevant facts about hydrodynamic lubrication theory in general.

This theory is based on the Reynolds equation which, for a time-independent clearance width $h(x, z)$, can be written

$$\frac{\partial}{\partial x}\left(\frac{\varrho h^3}{\mu}\frac{\partial p}{\partial x}\right) + \frac{\partial}{\partial z}\left(\frac{\varrho h^3}{\mu}\frac{\partial p}{\partial z}\right) = 6K\,\frac{\partial(\varrho h)}{\partial x}, \tag{3}$$

where K refers to tangential motion of the boundaries. I recall that eqn. (1) follows* from the fundamental Navier-Stokes equations of fluid motion, and the following two approximations: (i) inertial forces and gravity are negligible (Stokes flow approximation), and (ii) the flow is nearly parallel (boundary layer approximation). In the important special case $h(x, z) = h_0 = $ const. of a Hele-Shaw cell, eqn. (3) simplifies (Ref. 6, p. 582) to

$$\nabla^2 p = 0, \tag{3'}$$

provided that the density ϱ and the viscosity μ are constant.

As is observed in Ref. 15, section 1, various physically reasonable *fixed* boundary problems of hydrodynamic lubrication theory are mathematically well-set. For instance, this is so if the pressure is maintained at given levels along specified oil grooves, or if the oil flow rate from them is maintained at specified levels. This is a consequence of the general theory of linear elliptic partial differential equations like (3).

However, in heavily loaded bearings, the preceding mathematically well-set boundary value problem may predict negative pressure in diverging clearance spaces, thus violating condition (2a). Alternatively, if air has access to the clearance space, it may move the boundaries of the fully lubricated region by displacing oil. In either case, we have the well-known problem of *partial lubrication* with unknown 'free boundaries', of which the problem described in section 1 is a special case.

The situation is very analogous to the problem of predicting cavities and wakes in liquids of low viscosity, which was discussed by PLESSET (p. 1), GARABEDIAN (p. 30) and TULIN (p. 55). Indeed, these authors assumed (2a) or (2b), replacing the differential equation (3) by the Laplace equation for the velocity potential—

---

* See Ref. 7, Ch. I. For critical discussions of the derivation of eqn. (3), see Refs. 25–27.

References p. 120–121

the pressure and velocity being assumed related by the nonlinear Bernoulli equation $p + \frac{1}{2}\varrho\,(\nabla U) \cdot (\nabla U) =$ const., U being the velocity potential.

The resulting Helmholtz problem (Ref. 13, p. 261) has been studied by leading mathematicians and physicists for nearly a century; three recent monographs[1, 2, 3] survey what has been discovered by these scientists. My purpose is to call attention to an equally challenging class of free boundary problems for cavities in highly viscous fluids, and especially to those suggested by lubrication theory. In doing this, I shall lean heavily on ideas of Sir Geoffrey Taylor, trying to show what light pure mathematics can shed on them.

3. CAVITATION OR SEPARATION?

Various boundary conditions have been proposed for adapting the Reynolds equation (1) for infinite cylindrical bearings to conditions of partial lubrication. GUMBEL[28, 29] originally observed that the classical Sommerfeld solution for a journal bearing predicted negative pressures over much of the bearing, and proposed that these be replaced by a cavity at zero pressure. Because of the invariance of (1) under substitutions of the form $p \to p +$ const., this cavity may as well be assumed to begin at the *nip*, or point of minimum clearance. This condition has also been used by KNESCHKE[30].

However, as was observed by SWIFT[23] in a now classic paper: many other solutions of (1) are compatible with the boundary condition (2a); the boundary value problem defined by (1) and (2a) is not well-set. Swift derived the additional boundary condition

$$p'(x) = 0 \tag{4}$$

at the point where cavitation begins, from considerations of dynamical stability of a loaded bearing free to move. Condition (4) was derived independently by STIEBER[31, 32], as necessary for mass-conservation (continuity) at cavitation, if one assumes the Brillouin inequality (2a). Stieber's argument will be described in detail by Dr. Floberg; I will only comment here that a similar argument is needed to make the cavity problem in non-viscous fluids well-set (Ref. 1, p. 139). In any event, the Swift-Stieber boundary condition (4) is generally accepted in lubrication theory today.

Sir Geoffrey Taylor has already contrasted this condition with the condition assumed by HOPKINS and by PITTS AND GREILLER[20] in the study of liquid flow through rollers. This is really the old Prandtl separation condition in disguise: that *flow separation occurs where there is incipient counterflow*. He has shown that the Hopkins-Prandtl condition is appropriate for lightly loaded bearings, and has suggested that the Swift-Stieber condition is appropriate for heavily loaded bearings.

References p. 120–121

As FLOBERG will discuss these conditions again in his paper (p. 138), I shall make only a few remarks about them here.

First, I want to emphasize how natural it is to confuse cavitation with separation: the free boundary condition of constant pressure applies to both. For this reason, what are today[1, 2] called *cavities*, were considered to be *wakes* arising from flow separation* until 1940. And much earlier HELMHOLTZ, in his pioneer paper on 'Helmholtz flows', motivated his assumption of flow *separation* by observing that the Euler-Lagrange flow of an incompressible fluid past a sharp corner would have infinite negative pressure there, and that this would lead to *cavitation*.

Cavitation number

At high Reynolds numbers, the distinction between flow separation and cavitation is usually associated with the Thoma cavitation number (Ref. 1, p. 8)

$$Q = (p - p_v)/\tfrac{1}{2}\varrho U^2. \tag{5}$$

It would seem desirable to have an analogous cavitation number to distinguish lubricant cavitation from separation in cylindrical bearings having a time-independent clearance space. To do this, one might argue as follows.

In plane Poiseuille flow, $| \, dp/dx \, |$ is of the order of $\mu F/d^3$. When $h(x) = d + x^2/2r + \ldots$, the distance over which this is true is of the order of $\sqrt{rd}$. Hence the maximum pressure variation Δp_{max} in a cylindrical bearing should be of the order of

$$| \, dp/dx \, |_{max} \sqrt{rd} = \mu G r^{1/2} d^{-5/2} = \gamma \mu U r^{1/2} d^{-3/2},$$

where G is the mass-flow rate and γ is of order one (see section 4). The appropriate *cavitation number for lubrication* would therefore seem to be

$$C = p_a d^{3/2}/\mu U r^{1/2}. \tag{6}$$

For rollers having radii r_1 and r_2, one would set $r = r_1 r_2/(r_1 + r_2)$; in a journal bearing, $r = r_1 r_2/(r_1 - r_2)$.

4. THE FLOW NUMBER

I shall now summarize the main conclusions of Ref. 15 for the free boundary problem stated in section 1. These apply to sliding or rolling infinite cylindrical bearings with stationary axes; it is assumed that the region filled with lubricant extends from $x = a$ to $x = b$, as in Fig. 1. The analysis of Ref. 15 centers around the dimensionless *flow number*

$$\gamma = F/(U + V)d, \tag{7}$$

---

* Compare the terminology in the first edition of MILNE-THOMSON's *Theoretical Hydrodynamics* with that of later editions.

References p. 120–121

defined as the ratio of the oil flow rate F (area per unit time), divided by twice the average peripheral velocity times the minimum clearance width d.

In such a bearing, each of conditions (2a) and (2b) implies with (1) the integral relation

$$6\mu(U + V) \int_a^b \left(\frac{2\gamma d}{h^3} - \frac{1}{h^2}\right) dx = p(b) - p(a) = 0. \tag{8}$$

Conversely, if (8) holds, then one can construct a solution of (1) having the flow number γ which satisfies, at $x = a$ and $x = b$, (2b) or the first condition of (2a).

If $d \ll r$, one can set $h = d + x^2/2r$ to a good approximation. In this (parabolic) approximation, one gets for each γ a single dimensionless pressure function

$$P = [p(x) - p(0)] (d^3/2r)^{1/2}/\mu U = P(\xi), \quad \xi = x/\sqrt{rd}; \tag{9}$$

sample curves of $P(\xi)$ are plotted in Fig. 2. For each $\gamma > 0.5$, there exists a one-parameter family of choices of $\alpha = a/\sqrt{rd}$ for which (8) can be satisfied; hence

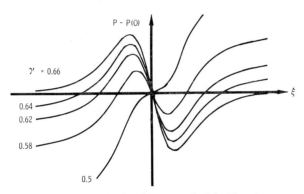

Fig. 2. Pressure distributions on cylindrical bearings.

the free boundary problem of section 1 has a two-parameter family of solutions, depending on γ and α.

However, the range of values of γ which is compatible with (8) is limited by the condition that $dp/dx > 0$ when $h = d$ (otherwise $dp/dx < 0$ for $h \neq d$), and by the condition

$$\int_0^\infty dp \leq 0.$$

Hence the limits are $\frac{1}{2} < \gamma \leq \frac{2}{3}$. The range of values of γ which is compatible with the Swift-Stieber condition (4) is $0.5 < \gamma < 0.613$ for a slider or roller bearing. To satisfy the Hopkins-Prandtl condition of no counterflow, one must have $0.550 < \gamma < 0.627$ for a slider bearing, and $0.591 < \gamma < 0.651$ for a roller bearing.

References p. 120–121

These results imply the following simple fact: *in partial lubrication, infinite cylindrical bearings will almost certainly be starved or flooded*: a very fine control of the oil flow rate is required to avoid these conditions. Hence the most interesting case is that of a flooded bearing (effectively $a = -\infty$) with some side-leakage before the pressure build-up begins.

The preceding results also raise the following deeper question: how accurately can the pressure distribution in partial lubrication be determined from Reynolds' equation (3) and boundary conditions on the pressure like (2a) or (2b)? FLOBERG AND JAKOBSSON (Ref. 11, p. 753) have found experimental agreement within $\pm 4\%$ under some conditions. I shall consider this question in Part B of the present paper from the theoretical standpoint.

5. HELE-SHAW CAVITY PROBLEM

Viewed from one side, the air-filled cavity between two rollers resembles superficially* a cavity 'fingering' its way as in Fig. 3 up a Hele-Shaw cell, or

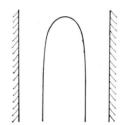

Fig. 3. A cavity in a Hele-Shaw cell.

narrow rectangular cell filled with viscous liquid. This 'fingering' has been studied by SAFFMAN AND TAYLOR[22], assuming Reynolds' approximation (3'). That is,

$$\nabla^2 p = 0, \tag{10}$$

where the average flow velocity $\mathbf{u}_{av}(x, z) = -\alpha \nabla p$, where $\alpha = h^2/12\mu$. On the free boundary of the cavity, $p = \text{const.}$ by (2a) or (2b); the cavity boundary may thus be expected to move** so as to make $\mathbf{u}(x, z) = -\alpha \nabla p$ there, where $\partial p/\partial n = 0$ on the channel side-walls.

Saffman and Taylor have obtained a one-parameter family of cavity profiles penetrating without change of form, of which the simplest (a straight line) is certainly unstable. They have asked which member of this family is stable. They have also observed that, in an infinite Hele-Shaw cell having a nearly

---

* *Caution.* The role of the narrow dimension is reversed; a better analogy will be described in section 8.

** Assuming that a negligible amount of liquid adheres to the wall in the cavity-filled region.

References p. 120–121

uniform pressure gradient, a circular or elliptic bubble of constant volume will translate without change of form. Its velocity will be $(1 + k)/k$ times that of the surrounding liquid, where $k =$ (virtual mass of bubble)/(mass of liquid displaced).

I should like to make some remarks about the analogous but mathematically simpler problem of cavity growth in an infinite Hele-Shaw cell, the entire region between two parallel plates of infinite extent. In this case, p is given (up to an additive constant and a factor of proportionality) by the conductor potential of the cavity. For such a growing (or shrinking) cavity, then, the normal velocity u_n of the cavity boundary will satisfy

$$u_n = \beta \partial \phi / \partial n, \tag{11}$$

where ϕ is the conductor potential of the cavity and β is a factor of proportionality.

Conditions (10)–(11) define from any given initial cavity profile $\Gamma(A_0)$, a one-parameter family of cavity profiles $\Gamma(A)$ depending on area. Such a family of profiles I shall call a *harmonic curve family*. The 'Hele-Shaw cavity problem' is the problem of finding $\Gamma(A)$, as defined above, given $\Gamma(A_0)$. It should be emphasized that, in formulating the Hele-Shaw cavity problem, one assumes that the pressure drop through the interface is constant, and neglects the residual liquid adhering to the solid walls bounding a cavity.

In space one can define the notion of a harmonic family of closed surfaces similarly—also by Eqs. (10)–(11). In a homogeneous porous medium filled with viscous liquid, the boundary of a cavity under high pressure (high enough so that gravity and surface tension can be neglected), considered as a function of time, should constitute such a harmonic surface family (see Ref. 33).

6. ELLIPTIC CAVITIES: VARIATIONAL PROPERTIES

One would naturally guess that, for a cavity growing from a small bubble to a large size, the asymptotic shape would be a circle in two dimensions and a sphere in three. However, this guess is incorrect because of the following surprising result.

THEOREM. In the plane, the similar ellipses

$$x^2 + y^2/(e^2 - 1) = a^2 \tag{12}$$

form a harmonic curve family for any fixed eccentricity e. In space, the similar (concentric, coaxial) ellipsoids

$$x^2 + y^2/\beta^2 + z^2/\gamma^2 = a^2 \tag{13}$$

form a harmonic surface family for any β, γ.

References p. 120–121

Sketch of proof. The preceding result merely states in different words a classic property of the conductor potential of ellipsoids, and its relation to ellipsoidal homoeoids.

Namely (Ref. 16, pp. 22 and 188–91), the conductor potential ϕ of any ellipsoid Γ: $x^2/a^2 + y^2/b^2 + z^2/c^2 = 1$ is the potential of a single layer whose charge is proportional to the thickness of the ellipsoidal homoeoid between Γ and the ellipsoid Γ': $x^2/a^2 + y^2/b^2 + z^2/c^2 = 1 + \varepsilon$, as $\varepsilon \downarrow 0$. But (Ref. 16, p. 164, Thm. 6), $\partial\phi/\partial n$ jumps from zero to an amount also proportional to this thickness. Hence the infinitesimal normal displacement required to expand Γ into Γ' is proportional to $\partial\phi/\partial n$, as required by (11).

The preceding result makes me think it unlikely that the empirical value $m = \frac{1}{2}$ in a channel, found in Ref. 22, can be deduced from the assumptions (10)–(11) of the Hele-Shaw problem, by stability or any other considerations.

Variational properties

Kelvin's Theorem (Ref. 6, section 344) implies that the conductor potential minimizes

$$\oint_\Gamma \nabla p \cdot \nabla p \, dR = - \oint_\Gamma \mathbf{u} \cdot \nabla p \, dR,$$

the rate at which work is done on the liquid by the expanding cavity, relative to all other volume-preserving fluid motions having the same normal velocity on the boundary. Intuition suggests that this choice of u_n also minimizes the rate at which work is done, for any given net rate $\dot{V} = \oint u_n dS$ of volumetric cavity expansion (*cf.* Ref. 34). This minimum rate of work is $\dot{V}/C$, where C is the electrostatic capacity of the cavity.

It would seem to follow that, to minimize the total work done in expanding a given cavity from volume V_0 to volume V_1 in given time, one must let the intermediate cavity shapes form a harmonic family of closed surfaces—at least (*cf.* ellipsoids *vs.* spheres) if V_1 is not much bigger than V_0.

Reversibility

The preceding formulation of the Hele-Shaw cavity problem is obviously invariant under the substitutions $\mathbf{u} \to -\mathbf{u}$, $p \to K(t) - p$. One may well ask: is this mathematical reversibility matched by approximate physical reversibility in a real Hele-Shaw cell? If one blows air into a bubble between parallel plates and then sucks it back out, does the bubble pass through the same configurations while contracting as while expanding? Certainly, the conditions for Taylor instability are reversed.

7. RELATED PROBLEMS

Many interesting free boundary problems besides the two discussed in sections 2–6 are associated with cavitation and separation in oil films (Reynolds' equation).

For example, one can study the time-dependent behavior of an oil film between two rotating cylinders, associated with a variable oil supply. It is conceivable that there might exist a continuous range of equilibrium boundary locations—say, the entire range between the Hopkins-Prandtl and Swift-Stieber boundary conditions, in a lightly loaded bearing. Donald Hays and I have considered this question, and have the following untested conditions to propose for determining the (free) boundaries $a(t)$ and $b(t)$ of the fully lubricated zone, in the case of an infinite cylindrical slider bearing with time-independent clearance width $h(x)$, when the oil feed rate is time-dependent.

The problem is to determine $a'(t)$ and $b'(t)$ as functions of $a(t)$ and $b(t)$ and the dimensionless oil *feed* rate $\gamma_f(t)$. This will not be the same as the dimensionless oil *flow* rate $\gamma(t)$, which is determined mathematically by the Reynolds equation (1) for given $a(t)$ and $b(t)$ by the condition $p(a) = p(b)$. Clearly two quite different conditions are required:

(a) *Upstream* boundary. Physically, it is natural to suppose that the dimensionless thickness $\omega_u(t)$ and $\omega_v(t)$ of the oil layer carried by each surface is given. One then compares the oil feed rate $U\omega_u(t) + V\omega_v(t) = (U + V)\,\gamma_f(t)$ with the oil flow rate $(U + V)\,\gamma(t)$, both divided by d. If $\gamma_f(t) > \gamma(t)$, then oil will accumulate upstream at the rate $(U + V)\,(\gamma_f - \gamma)d$ and the boundary of the fully lubricated zone should move upstream at a rate

$$-a'(t) = (U + V)\,(\gamma_f - \gamma)d/[h - d\omega_u - d\omega_v].$$

Whereas if $\gamma_f(t) < \gamma(t)$, then one may reasonably expect the boundary to move downstream. Assuming $h'(a) < 0$ (if $h'(a) > 0$, film rupture is presumably complete), the flow velocity $u(y, t)$ is however greatest on the solid surfaces in the Reynolds approximation. Hence, although common sense suggests that $a'(t) \simeq (U + V)/2$, it is very difficult to picture $u(y, t)$ in the vicinity of the separation point. In this case, therefore, it may be impossible to predict $a'(t)$ without considering deviations from the Reynolds approximation—*i.e.*, without invoking Part B.

(b) *Downstream* boundary. In the case of a lightly loaded bearing, for which $p > p_v$ everywhere, it is attractive to speculate that $b'(t) = u_m(t) = \min_y u\,(b, y, t)$ in accordance with the Prandtl-Hopkins condition. Moreover one can speculate that the film above the y_m minimizing $u(b, y, t)$ adheres to the upper surface, and that the rest adheres to the lower surface, each being transported downstream with the velocity of the adjacent boundary (U or V). The thicknesses of the films would be, correspondingly:

$$H_u = \left[\int_0^{y_m} (u - u_m)\, \mathrm{d}y \right]/U, \qquad H_v = \left[\int_{y_m}^{h(b)} (u - u_m)\, \mathrm{d}y \right]/V.$$

However, these are very speculative hypotheses.

Internal cavities

Again, one has the problem of explaining mathematically the internal cavities which form in divergent clearance spaces under a rotating cylinder or over a sliding plane. This problem has been studied by COLE AND HUGHES (Ref. 17; Ref. II, pp. 147–50), by McBROOM[35] and by DOWSON (Ref. II, pp. 93–9). The conclusions of these authors have been critically analyzed by FLOBERG AND JAKOBSSON (Ref. II, pp. 753–5). Since FLOBERG contributes to this Symposium himself (p. 138), I shall only make one comment on this problem here: many of the difficulties which plague one arise in the study of cavitation in slightly viscous liquids as well—see for example Ref. I, Ch. XV, sections 1–3.

Specifically, the formulation of a physically realistic and mathematically well-set boundary value problem for predicting such internal cavities is troubled by the effects of air in solution, and by the roles of cavitation nuclei and surface tension—about which I shall say more in Part B.

Finally, it is qualitatively obvious that cavitation can occur in lubricating films when two parallel plates are pulled apart with great force. This is the reverse of the *squeeze film problem* (Ref. 7, Ch. 7), in which $\dot{h} < 0$. It represents a laboratory idealization of a problem which can arise in a dynamically loaded bearing, and to which the Gumbel device (section 1) of simply ignoring negative pressures is applied at present (Ref. 7, p. 238ff.). Here again the general difficulties mentioned in Ref. I, Ch. XV, sections 1–3, arise. The presence of cavitation nuclei along scratches is especially evident; because of the short time-scale for diffusion, air in solution is less important. In addition, the oil behavior seems strongly affected by the Taylor instability of the interfaces between expanding oil vapor and contracting lubricant. As this problem will be discussed by HAYS AND FEITEN (p. 122), I will say no more about it here.

B. MORE EXACT MODELS

8. INTRODUCTION

As was stated in section 2, the Reynolds equation (1) of Part A has been applied successfully to many lubrication problems, in spite of the drastic approximations made in deriving it. Its most conspicuous failures are associated with the boundary conditions which determine where separation and cavitation occur in partial lubrication. For example, one does not know whether to assume the Swift-Stieber condition or the Prandtl-Hopkins condition—though the former seems better for lightly loaded and the latter for heavily loaded bearings. On the edge of internal cavities, moreover, where the transition from inflow to outflow conditions may be abrupt, one does not know that either defines a well-set problem—even in time-independent flow. Finally, it is certain that the boundary layer approximation of nearly parallel flow is not reasonable on the edges where the oil film makes contact or separates: the nominal 'reverse flow' against an adverse pressure gradient is incompatible with the hypothesis of a stationary interface, for example.

The remainder of my paper will be devoted to discussing some boundary value problems whose solution might help to clarify some of the above uncertainties, and hence to make possible a rigorous hydrodynamic theory of partial lubrication.

This discussion will involve two questions of a very different character about each problem. Is it well-set? And is it mathematically tractable: can one compute an approximate solution?

For simplicity (to reduce the number of independent variables), I will discuss (except in section 12) only time-independent plane flow in infinite cylindrical bearings, conditions being supposed independent of t and z. Moreover I will continue to accept most of Reynolds' approximations, concentrating my attention on those which seem to me most dubious: the boundary layer approximation and neglect of surface tension.

9. DISCUSSION OF APPROXIMATIONS

In solving the Reynolds equation, or the Navier-Stokes equations from which it is derived, one usually assumes that μ and ϱ are constant. Actually, both vary with the pressure and the temperature. The decrease in μ by frictional heating is often important for oil films, and variations in ϱ play an essential role in the theory of gas lubrication (Ref. 3; Ref. 7, Ch. 5). However, as I do not have any constructive ideas about treating the nonlinear problems associated with variables μ and ϱ, and as μ and ϱ are nearly constant in many applications, I shall assume them to be constant below.

Likewise, I shall ignore the effects of the nonlinear momentum-convection term in the Navier-Stokes equations; for its effects, which can be important, see Ref. 7, Ch. 12.

By ignoring the preceding nonlinear effects, I shall be assuming in effect the approximation of Stokes flow (or 'creeping' flow), which is valid at low Reynolds numbers in liquids of constant viscosity at moderate pressures. In section 10, I shall formulate two free boundary problems for Stokes flows, which appear to me to be interesting and, in principle, mathematically tractable.

In the problems just mentioned, surface tension and gravity are assumed negligible; sections 11–12 will be devoted to analyzing the important but often forgotten role which they play in cavitation and flow separation of viscous layers in channels. In section 13, this analysis will be followed by a discussion of the mysterious phenomenon of capillary friction.

Finally, in section 14, I will discuss briefly the proper mathematical treatment of dissolved gas and gas nuclei, whose importance for cavitation and boiling in slightly viscous liquids has already been described by PLESSET (p. 1).

10. STOKES FLOWS WITH FREE BOUNDARIES

As stated in sections 2, 9, the Stokes flow approximation arises if one omits the boundary layer assumption of nearly parallel flow from those usually made in deriving the Reynolds approximation. Since this assumption is seldom plausible in the immediate vicinity of a separation point, the formulation and solution of well-set boundary value problems for Stokes flows would seem a necessary preliminary to the rigorous derivation of accurate boundary conditions for partial lubrication.

For incompressible time-independent plane flows, the Stokes flow approximation (the Navier-Stokes equations with momentum-convection neglected) reduces to

$$\nabla p = \mu \nabla^2 \mathbf{u}, \qquad \mathbf{u} = (\partial \psi / \partial x, \ -\partial \psi / \partial y), \tag{14}$$

where $\psi(x, y)$ is the stream function. Taking the curl of both sides, we get $0 = \mu \nabla^4 \psi$, or

$$\nabla^4 \psi = 0. \tag{15}$$

Taking the divergence of (14), we get $\nabla^2 p = 0$ since $\nabla \cdot \mathbf{u} = 0$. But taking the curl of the second equation of (14), we also see that the vorticity $\zeta(x, y) = \nabla^2 \psi$—and, comparing the gradient of this equation with the first equation of (14), that $\mu \zeta$ and p are conjugate harmonic functions.

To define a well-set boundary value problem, the preceding differential equations must be supplemented by suitable boundary conditions. On any solid wall, one has the usual (Ref. 6, Art. 357) fixed boundary conditions $\psi = \text{const.}$, $\partial \psi / \partial n = 0$, which can be combined into the single vector equation

$$\nabla \psi = \mathbf{0} \quad \text{on any fixed boundary.} \tag{16}$$

On a free boundary, the simplest physically interesting hypothesis is that of constant pressure and zero shear stress, which amounts to neglecting surface tension and gravity. In other words, the simplest free boundary conditions are:

$$\partial p / \partial s = \partial \zeta / \partial n = 0 \quad \text{and} \quad \partial^2 \psi / \partial n^2 = 0. \tag{17}$$

Among the simplest configurations which define physically interesting free boundary problems, are those sketched in Figs. 4a and 4b below.

Fig. 4a refers to a plane sliding past a parallel semi-infinite block at constant velocity U. The fixed boundary conditions (16) amount to

$$\psi = 0, \ \partial\psi/\partial y = U \quad \text{on} \quad y = 0,$$
$$\psi = \partial\psi/\partial y = 0 \qquad \text{on} \quad y = d, x \leq 0. \tag{18}$$

The dimensionless flow rate $\gamma = \psi(x, d)/Ud$ is an important parameter; $\gamma = \frac{1}{2}$ if there is no upstream pressure gradient. For general γ, we have the asymptotic conditions:

$$\psi \sim Uy, \ 0 \leq y \leq \gamma d, \quad \text{as} \quad x \to +\infty \ (\text{downstream})$$
$$\psi \sim U[y - (2 - 3\gamma)y^2/d + (2\gamma - 1)y^3/d^2] \quad \text{as} \quad x \to -\infty. \tag{18'}$$

Fig. 4b refers to the equilibrium of a two-dimensional cavity in the channel between two parallel plates sliding with velocity U. The most interesting questions concern

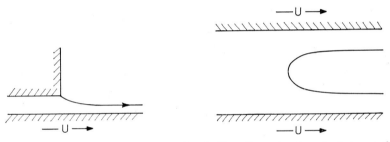

Fig. 4a. Stokes flow under block.   Fig. 4b. Two-dimensional cavity between plates.

the pressure gradient required to maintain equilibrium of the cavity location, the relative thickness $2\delta/d$ of the two layers sliding downstream with the plates, and the stability of equilibrium. Analogs of conditions (18)–(18') are easily written down for given pressure gradient and layer thickness δ.

It is, of course, not obvious *a priori* that either of the preceding boundary value problems is well-set. My 'physical intuition' suggests that they are, at least for suitable ranges of the parameter γ involved (or, equivalently, U and d).

It would be very interesting to know what these ranges were, and to determine $\Psi(\xi, \eta; \gamma) = \psi(d\xi, d\eta)/Ud$. In the problem of Fig. 4a, one would also like to know the contact angle α at the separation point as a function of γ, and to know how far one had to go upstream before the Reynolds approximation gave the flow velocity up to $\pm 0.001U$ (say).

The preceding problems have interesting generalizations, sketched in Figs. 5a–5b. Fig. 5a refers to a plane sliding past a tilted block, and Fig. 5b to two parallel planes sliding with different velocities U and V, which need not have the same sign.

One can also generalize the preceding problems to the axially symmetric case. In the problem corresponding to Fig. 4a, this involves an annular region, and is not too interesting. But the problem of Fig. 4b generalizes to that of a bubble penetrating a tube: the problem studied by Taylor and Saffman; its solution would be most interesting.

Methods of solution

It is natural to try to solve the preceding problems by numerical relaxation (or overrelaxation) methods, analogous to those used by SIR RICHARD SOUTHWELL[36] to solve the Helmholtz problem. However, more rigorous results could probably be obtained by transforming the problem to a (linear) integral equation on the boundary condition, and extending to these free boundary problems the methods used so effectively by MUSKHELISHVILII[37] and his school in two-dimensional

Fig. 5a. Generalization of Fig. 4a.   Fig. 5b. Generalization of Fig. 4b.

elasticity theory. For making such an extension, it would be very helpful to have a *reflection principle* for the biharmonic equation and the boundary conditions $u = \partial u/\partial y = 0$ on $y = 0$, analogous to that for solutions of the Laplace and Helmholtz equations (see Ref. 38) with $u = 0$. For $u = \partial^2 u/\partial y^2 = 0$ (a straight streamline at zero shear), the analog is obvious: $u(x, -y) = u(x, y)$. But for the boundary conditions $u = \partial u/\partial y = 0$, the domain of analytic continuability seems hard to ascertain.

Historical remarks

Unfortunately, the literature on Stokes flows with free boundaries is very meager, and I know of no previous discussion of the problem of Fig. 4a.

The problem of Fig. 4b and its axially symmetric analog concern 'fingering'; these problems are analogous to that of Taylor and Saffman, and discussed in section 5. It may be hoped that this problem, which has been shown by Taylor and Saffman to be not well-set (to have a two-parameter family of solutions) in the Hele-Shaw approximation, is well-set in the Stokes flow approximation. It has also been considered by BANKS AND MILL[14] and by COX[24].

Though PITTS AND GREILLER[20] solve the problem defined by (15), (16), and the first condition of (17) for an assumed parabolic meniscus, their solution fails to satisfy the second condition of (17): the meniscus assumed is not a free boundary*. Indeed, the prevailing view seems to be that the rigorous solution of free boundary problems for Stokes flows is impracticable.

Viewed in historical perspective, I think this opinion is unduly pessimistic. Fifty years ago, boundary value problems were not considered solvable unless their solution could be expressed in terms of a limited family of 'special functions'. At that time, Sommerfeld's solution of the Reynolds equation for the periodic domain between two circular cylinders was considered to be on the frontier of the tractable, and the general treatment of finite bearings to be impractical. Today, with modern computing machines and modern computing methods, the solution of finite bearing problems is considered relatively routine (Ref. 7, Ch. 4).

Extrapolating, it seems reasonable to think that many problems considered impossibly difficult today will be considered routine fifty years from now. I do not think that the problems which I have just described are much more difficult, in principle, than analogous free boundary problems for slightly viscous fluids which have yielded to a concentrated mathematical attack (see Refs. 1, 2) during the past twenty years.

II. SURFACE TENSION

The importance for lubrication of capillary forces (surface energy) is well known. For example, it has long been suspected** that the quality of 'oiliness', or of forming a monomolecular adsorbed layer on a solid surface, may help avoid seizing. The importance of capillary forces for inhibiting or reducing cavitation is also well known; see Ref. 1, Ch. XV, section 3, for a brief survey of the facts.

However, little attention has been paid to the effect of surface tension on the solution of free boundary problems of viscous flow.

An important exception is provided by a recent paper of PEARSON[19], who has studied the detachment from a divergent wedge with divergence angle α, of a viscous liquid spread over a plane surface (see Fig. 6). He has plotted the observed separation point (Ref. 19, Fig. 11) as a function of $\tau = 2\alpha/S = 2\sigma\alpha/\mu U$. His main conclusion is that, if $\tau < 0.03$, then one can predict the location of the observed separation point $x = b$ by combining the Hopkins-Prandtl separation

---

* A similar objection applies to existing models for 'creeping jets' (Ref. 1, p. 273).
** Ref. 39. For modern views see Refs. 40, 41.

condition with eqn. (2b) of section 1, modified to $p(b) = p(a) - 2\sigma/h(b)$ to allow for surface tension.

To take surface tension into account in the free boundary problems of section 10, one must modify the first free boundary condition of (17) to

$$\partial p/\partial s = \partial \zeta/\partial n = \sigma \partial (1/r)/\partial s, \tag{17'}$$

where $1/r$ is the local boundary curvature.

For the problems of section 10, one naturally guesses that the position of the free boundary, and the solution, can be expanded in a power series involving the reciprocal $1/S = \sigma/U\mu$ of the Taylor-Saffman parameter $S = U\mu/\sigma$, which is clearly the relevant dimensionless parameter. (Note that $S = W/Re$ is the ratio of the Weber number $W = \varrho U^2 d/\sigma$ to the Reynolds number $Re = \varrho U d/\mu$.)

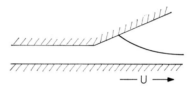

Fig. 6. Flow separation from wedge.

In the problems of Part A (or, if one extends the block of Fig. 4a to an infinite plane), the solution depends on another physical parameter. This is the angle of contact between the meniscus and the upper surface at the point of contact. This is often not accurately predictable, though conventional discussions (*cf.* Ref. 8, Vol. 1, p. 30) often attempt to deduce it from supposed constants characterizing the interfacial energy per unit area of the liquid-gas, liquid-solid, and solid-gas interfaces near the line of triple contact.

In conclusion, then, one wishes to solve boundary value problems corresponding to the geometrical configurations of Part A, but assuming that the pressure is a biharmonic function which satisfies (17') on the boundary, and that the angle of contact is given.

12. STABILITY

It is well known that free boundaries in slightly viscous fluids are extremely unstable, and that the main limitations on this instability are provided by surface tension and viscosity*. If it were not for these stabilizing influences, the interface would be infinitely unstable.

It has been observed by Taylor and Saffman (Ref. 13, p. 287) that an analogous situation arises when air or a liquid of low viscosity displaces a fluid of higher

---

* See Ref. 42 and the refs. listed there in ftnts. 11, 12.

viscosity ın a Hele-Shaw cell. If the simple mathematical model of sections 5–6 is used, infinite instability is predicted.

It would be interesting to find out what limits are imposed on this predicted instability by the Stokes flow model of section 9 and surface tension. These may be expected to play stabilizing roles like those played by surface tension and viscosity in the stability theory of Helmholtz flows. The author suspects that, in addition to the Taylor-Saffman parameter S, the ratio d/a of the thickness of a Hele-Shaw cell to its width may be relevant to this problem.

A possibly related instability arises when a layer of viscous fluid separates from a solid surface in a diverging clearance space. This phenomenon has also been studied by PEARSON, who has plotted in (Ref. 21, Fig. 10) the number of crests per inch* in the flutings which are observed near the line of separation, as a function of the variable τ. He has correlated these results with a mathematical model in which surface tension counteracts the destabilizing influence of the viscous pressure gradient. Pearson also discusses the ribbed appearance of the liquid surface where it separates from cylindrical rollers and sliders, which he explains similarly.

My own intuitive impression, based on visual observations of oil films behind a cylindrical slider at the General Motors Research Laboratories, is somewhat different. My feeling is that the adverse pressure gradient (which would not exist if Swift's condition were fulfilled) sucks air into the zone of separation, and that the upper solid attracts the liquid**. The flutings are, I think, symptomatic of a secondary flow which increases the flow of lubricant by decreasing the area of contact between the moving oil and the stationary upper surface. The role of surface tension is to maintain differences in pressure causing this secondary flow; I do not think of it as really stabilizing.

13. CAPILLARY FRICTION

It is evident that the free boundary problems defined in section 1 are going to be very tough to solve. And even these very complicated mathematical problems may not be completely realistic in many cases, because real capillary forces are often strongly influenced by small impurities, and by capillary friction (or 'surface viscosity') as well.

Capillary friction may be associated with the creation and destruction of liquid-gas interfaces and of liquid-solid interfaces. Either type can be ascribed to the free energy of a surface film formed by preferential adsorption on the interface

---

* Dimensional analysis suggests that the wave-length divided by $h(b)$ might be a more appropriate dependent variable.

** It would be interesting to see the effect of using an oil repellent upper surface!

References p. 120–121

of some special ingredient in a solution or a mixture. Such a film may behave like a plastic solid or (in the case of liquid-gas interfaces) like a viscous liquid *.

Various opinions have been expressed regarding surface viscosity. REYNOLDS (Ref. 9, Vol. 1, pp. 410–12) stated that it was negligible. But it was postulated by BOUSSINESQ[43], and has recently been used by EISENMENGER AND MEYER (Ref. 12, pp. 179–200) to explain the dynamic response of bubbles to oscillating pressure fields.

Capillary friction seems sometimes to behave like Coulomb friction (in 'solid surface films'?), opposing the formation and destruction of interfacial area by a constant force, and sometimes like viscous friction (in 'liquid surface films'?). The hysteresis of the contact angle, which has been frequently observed and explained'**, seems not unnaturally to conform better to the former hypothesis.

REFERENCES

1 G. BIRKHOFF AND E. H. ZARANTONELLO, *Jets, Wakes, and Cavities*, Academic Press, New York, 1957.
2 D. GILBARG, Jets and Cavities, *Handbuch der Physik*, Vol. IX, Springer, Berlin, 1960 pp. 311–445.
3 W. GROSS, *Gas Film Lubrication*, Wiley, New York, 1962.
4 M. I. GUREVICH, *Teorie Strui Idealnoi Zhidkosti*, Governmental Agency for Physical-Mathematical Literature, Moscow, 1961.
5 O. D. KELLOGG, *Potential Theory*, Springer, Berlin, 1929.
6 H. LAMB, *Hydrodynamics*, 6th ed., Cambridge Univ. Press, London, 1932.
7 O. PINKUS AND B. STERNLICHT, *Theory of Hydrodynamic Lubrication*, McGraw-Hill, New York, 1961.
8 L. PRANDTL AND O. G. TIETJENS, *Hydro- and Aeromechanics*, 2 vols., McGraw-Hill, New York, 1934.
9 O. REYNOLDS, *Collected Scientific Papers*, 3 vols., Cambridge University Press. Vol. 2, pp. 228–310. Reprinted from. *Phil. Trans.* 177 (1886) 157–234.
10 J. J. STOKER, *Water Waves*, Interscience, New York, 1957.
11 *Conference on Lubrication and Wear*, published by the Institution of Mechanical Engineers, London, 1957.
12 *Cavitation in Hydrodynamics*, Proc. Symposium at the Natl. Phys. Lab., H.M. Stationery Office, London, 1955.
13 RALPH D. COOPER, editor, *Second Symposium on Naval Hydrodynamics, 1958*, Publ. ONR/ACR-38, U.S. Navy Dept., Washington, D.C.
14 W. H. BANKS AND C. C. MILL, Some Observations on the Behavior of Liquids between Rotating Cylinders, *Proc. Roy. Soc. (London)*, A223 (1954) 414–19.
15 G. BIRKHOFF AND D. F. HAYS, Free Boundaries in Partial Lubrication, *J. Math. Phys. (M.I.T.)*, 42, No. 2 (June 1963).
16 A. CAMERON AND W. L. WOOD, The Full Journal Bearing, *Trans. Inst. Mech. Eng.*, 161 (1949) 59–72.

---

* See Ref. 40, Chs. II-III; Ref. 41, p. 92 and (for surface viscosity) section 51.
** See Ref. 41, sections 142 and 255–8, where various 'explanations' are compared; Ref. 40, p. 181, and Ref. 44.

17 J. A. COLE AND C. J. HUGHES, Oil Film Extent in Complete Journal Bearings, *Proc. Inst. Mech. Engrs.*, 170 (1956) 499–510.

18 L. FLOBERG, The Infinite Journal Bearing Considering Vaporization, *Trans. Chalmers Univ. Technol., Gothenburg*, No. 189, 1957.

19 J. R. A. PEARSON, The Instability of Uniform Viscous Flow under Rollers and Spreaders, *J. Fluid Mech.*, 7 (1960) 481–500.

20 E. PITTS AND J. GREILLER, The Flow of Thin Liquid Films between Rollers, *J. Fluid Mech.*, 11 (1961) 33–50.

21 A. A. RAIMONDI AND J. BOYD. A Solution for a Finite Journal Bearing, *Trans. Am. Soc. Lub. Eng.*, 1 (1958) 194–209.

22 P. G. SAFFMAN AND SIR GEOFFREY TAYLOR, The Penetration of a Fluid into a Porous Medium or Hele-Shaw Cell Containing a more Viscous Liquid, *Proc. Roy. Soc. (London)*, A245 (1958) 312–29.

23 H. W. SWIFT, The Stability of Lubrication Films in Journal Bearings, *Proc. Inst. Civil Engrs. (London)*, 233 (1932) 267–88.

24 B. G. COX, On Driving a Viscous Fluid out of a Tube, *J. Fluid Mech.*, 14 (1962) 81–96.

25 G. H. WANNIER, *Quart. Appl. Math.*, 8 (1950) 1–32.

26 H. G. ELROD, *Quart. Appl. Math.*, 17 (1959) 349–59.

27 W. E. LANGLOIS, *Quart. Appl. Math.*, 20 (1962) 349–59.

28 L. GUMBEL, *Monatsch. Berl. Bez. VDI*, (1914) 97.

29 L. GUMBEL AND E. EVERLING, *Reibung und Schmierung im Maschinenbau*, Berlin, 1925.

30 KNESCHKE, *Ing.-Arch.*, 25 (1957) 227–43.

31 W. STIEBER, *Das Schwimmlager*, V.D.I., Berlin, 1933.

32 L. PRANDTL, *Proc. of a General Discussion on Lubrication and Lubricants*, Vol. 1, pp. 241–8, Inst. Mech. Engrs., London, 1937.

33 R. A. WOODING, *Z. angew. Math. Phys.*, 13 (1962) 255–65.

34 D. G. CHRISTOPHERSON, *The Engineer*, Jan. 18, 1957, p. 100.

35 H. L. MCBROOM, *Scientific Lubrication*, April, 1953.

36 R. V. SOUTHWELL, *Relaxation Methods in Theoretical Physics*, pp. 212–26; *Phil. Trans. Roy. Soc.*, 20 (1946) 117–61.

37 N. MUSKHELISHVILII, *Some Basic Problems of the Theory of Elasticity*, and *Singular Integral Equations*, Noordhoff, Groningen, 1953.

38 H. PORITSKY, *Trans. Am. Math. Soc.*, 59 (1946) 248–79.

39 T. E. STANTON, *Proc. Roy, Soc. (London)*, A 102 (1922) 241–55.

40 N. K. ADAM, *The Physics and Chemistry of Surfaces*, 3rd ed., Oxford, 1941, pp. 222–7.

41 J. J. BIKERMAN, *Surface Chemistry*, 2nd ed., Academic Press, 1958, p. 392.

42 G. BIRKHOFF, Helmholtz and Taylor Instability, *Proc. Symposia in Applied Math.*, Vol. XIII, Am. Math. Soc., 1962.

43 J. BOUSSINESQ, *Compt. Rend.*, 156 (1913) 1124 and 157 (1913) 313.

44 D. W. CRIDDLE, The Viscosity and Elasticity of Interfaces, *Rheology, Theory and Applications*, Vol. 3, edited by F. R. EIRICH, Academic Press, New York, 1960.

Cavities between Moving
Parallel Plates

DONALD F. HAYS AND JAMES B. FEITEN

Mechanical Development Department,
General Motors Research Laboratories, Warren, Michigan

INTRODUCTION

Under certain conditions thin viscous films of an incompressible fluid may become discontinuous, *i.e.*, they may either cavitate or exhibit flow separation. Such an occurrence complicates greatly the analytical treatment of problems in thin films because of the resulting 'free boundary' of the cavity. To effect a well-set boundary value problem, it then becomes necessary to furnish additional boundary conditions over those required for the solution of the more common problem with fixed boundaries. Since the formation of cavities is not uncommon in mechanisms or processes utilizing viscous films, it is important that greater knowledge be available regarding cavity behaviour and of the circumstances contributing to cavity growth and collapse. Consequently two programs were initiated toward this end, one being experimental in nature, the other being analytical. Because of the complexity of the problem it was decided that the physical system to be experimentally investigated should be as simple as possible so as to minimize the mathematical difficulties of the analysis. As a result of this requirement, the final system consisted of a circular optical flat which was maintained parallel to a flat steel surface, the gap between the two surfaces being filled with a viscous fluid. The optical flat was then pulled away from the steel surface and pictures were taken of the subsequent cavity growth with a high speed camera. The data obtained in this manner was then compared to the analytically predicted cavity behaviour.

In this paper the experimental work of the program is presented prior to the analytical phase. This order allows a fuller understanding of the complexities of the phenomena under investigation and gives a background from which a mathematical model can be formulated which will be meaningful and useful.

DESCRIPTION OF APPARATUS

A photograph of the machine used to generate cavities is shown in Fig. 1. The machine consists of a welded steel structure supporting a shaft and disk assembly, a circular optical flat held in a movable fixture, a cam and drive system, and the required instrumentation. A portion of the disk is visible in the photograph. The disk is 24 inches in diameter and is made of steel. A ground surface 2 inches wide extends inward from the disk circumference. It is between this ground surface and the back face of the optical flat that the cavity is created. A quartz

Fig. 1. Test machine used to study cavity formation in thin fluid films.

optical flat is used to form one boundary surface to permit viewing and photographic recording of a cavity in the fluid film.

The machine was designed to permit the study of cavity formation (1) in a diverging wedge with one surface carrying a fluid through the wedge, (2) between two separating surfaces with a fluid between them and the surfaces remaining parallel at all times, and (3) between two separating parallel surfaces with a fluid between them and one surface moving past the other at a constant velocity. In this investigation we are concerned only with the second process, *i.e.*, the surfaces are parallel and have a normal velocity.

Reference p. 137

Fig. 2 is a cut-away drawing of the test machine. Shown are the disk surface, the optical flat and its holder, the cam and its drive system, a degree timing wheel and an instrumented cantilever beam.

A portion of the optical flat holding fixture acts as a point cam follower. The optical flat holder and cam follower are connected to the steel base through two parallel spring steel plates. The spring plates serve a dual purpose: (1) they load the point follower against the cam, and (2) they act as a four bar linkage with flexure pivots to maintain the optical flat parallel to the disk surface at all times during the cam cycle. The cam operating against the point follower describes the rate of the separation of the optical flat from the ground disk surface.

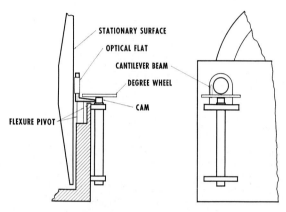

Fig. 2. Cut-away drawing showing components of the test machine.

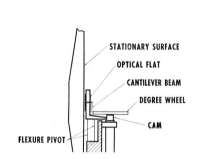

Fig. 3. Cutaway drawing showing details of the cantilever beam assembly used to monitor the clearance between the two flat parallel surfaces.

The degree timing wheel is attached to the top side of the cam and rotates with it. In this position it is visible in the movies taken to study the cavity growth process. The degree wheel is used to correlate cam position with cavity growth when the movies are studied. Fig. 3 shows in detail the cantilever beam assembly. The purpose of the cantilever beam is to give a continuous readout of the clearance between the disk surface and optical flat during each test cycle. The beam is instrumented with strain gages and is attached to the optical flat holder. The cantilever beam is actuated by a pin which passes through a hole in the optical flat holder. The beam is preloaded to hold the pin firmly against the disk surface. As the cam rotates it allows the optical flat and its holder to move away from the disk surface. This tends to unload the cantilever beam and therefore changes the output signal from the strain gages. The output from the beam is sent through two amplifiers connected in parallel and recorded on a two channel strip chart calibrated in inches of clearance. This instrumentation is shown in Fig. 4. The dual amplifiers permit taking traces at two magnifications, the higher magnification giving an accurate description of the rate of separation during the early part of the test cycle. A photograph of a typical chart is shown in Fig. 5. Along the top edge of the chart are timing marks at ten degree intervals. Zero degrees is at the extreme

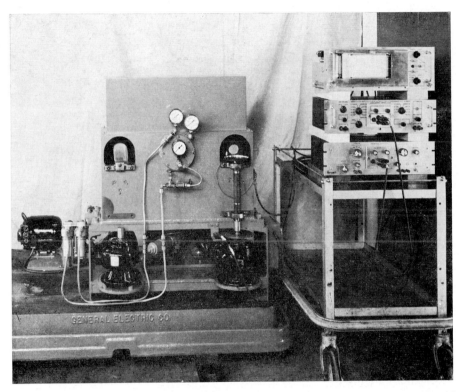

Fig. 4. Test machine and associated instrumentation used to record the rate of separation of the two flat parallel surfaces.

left. The upper trace is at a magnification of approximately 50 times size. It shows the rate of change of clearance between the two surfaces during a complete cycle. The lower trace is an 8 times magnification of the upper trace and permits a more accurate determination of the separation rate during the first half of the test cycle.

The drive cam rotates at the rate of one revolution per second. One cam cycle includes moving the optical flat away from the disk to a maximum clearance of about 0.020 inch and then returning the optical flat back to its original position

Reference p. 137

ready for the start of another cycle. In the tests run thus far the clearance at the start of a cycle has been approximately 0.0002 inch.

Viewing cavities in a thin oil film is very difficult due to the fact that thin oil films are nearly transparent even when dyes are added. The best method found to observe cavity growth in a thin oil film is to fluoresce the oil. The fluid used in

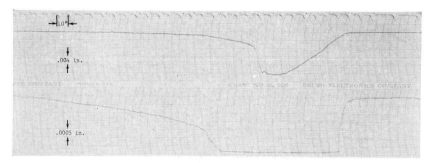

Fig. 5. Chart showing the rate of separation of the two parallel
surfaces for one test cycle.

the test machine is a petroleum base fluid and additives give it high penetrating and fluorescent qualities. The cavities, being void of the fluid, show up as dark areas in the bright field of fluoresced fluid. The liquid used has a specific gravity of 1.008 at 60° F, a viscosity of 15 centistokes at 80° F, and a surface tension of 34.9 dynes/cm at 74° F. The fluid is supplied to the space between the parallel plates by distribution tubes around the outer edge of the optical flat. Several jets distribute an excess of fluid completely around the cavity area.

TEST PROCEDURE

In setting up for a test the disk position is adjusted to give the desired initial clearance between the disk surface and the optical flat. The clearance space between the disk and the optical flat is then flooded with oil. When a test cycle begins, the cam rotates causing the two surfaces to separate at a rate sufficient to initiate and sustain a cavity in the oil film. The cavity occurs during the first 1/10 to 1/2 part of a cam cycle. Because the life of a cavity is so short, high speed photography is used to record its growth and collapse.

Fig. 6 is a photograph showing the set up for taking high speed movies. Mercury vapor lamps are used to fluoresce the fluid thereby making the cavity areas clearly visible in the thin oil film. A highly fluorescent fluid permits film speeds in excess of 7000 frames per second. This speed is more than adequate for critical studies of the growth and collapse of cavities in the oil film.

Reference p. 137

Fig. 6. Arrangement of lighting and camera for high-speed photography.

EXPERIMENTAL RESULTS

Fig. 7 is a sequence of photographs showing the growth and collapse of a cavity. The light colored circular area is the fluid between the two parallel surfaces viewed through the circular optical flat. The cavities show up in the photographs as darkened areas. In the first photograph cavity growth has just begun at several points in the oil film. The formation of these many cavities is completely random and is probably dependent upon conditions existing within the fluid which produce nucleation sites. Each of the cavities starts as a circular void. Subsequent growth from these circular voids is in the form of fingers which radiate out in all directions. In most instances there are additional stringer-like outgrowths from these radiating fingers. In this way each cavity takes on a very complex fern-like shape. Although each cavity tends to expand equally in all directions, their growth is affected by neighbouring cavities. When the boundaries of two or more cavities approach one another, the growth in that direction diminishes. Eventually, the cavities

Reference p. 137

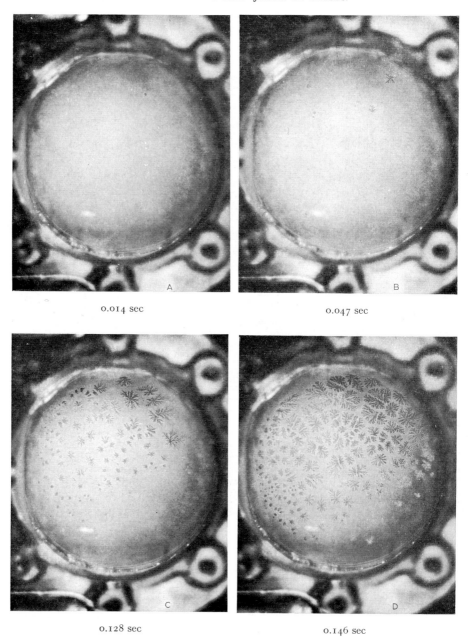

0.014 sec   0.047 sec

0.128 sec   0.146 sec

Fig. 7. (A–D). Photographs which are representative of the growth and collapse of a cavity in a thin fluid film. To assure the highest quality reproductions, the photographs shown are still shots taken during different test cycles.

Reference p. 137

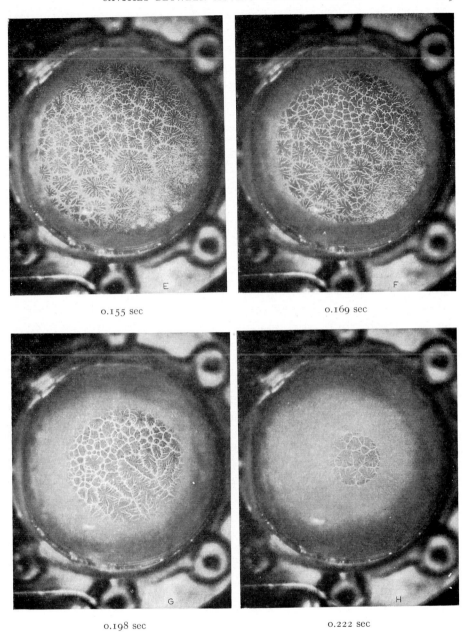

0.155 sec

0.169 sec

0.198 sec

0.222 sec

Fig. 7. (E–H).

fill in an area having a circular shape. At this point the pressure will be equal everywhere in the circular area and the area can then be considered to be a single cavity. In the fifth photograph the cavity has reached its maximum size. In photographs five through eight the two parallel surfaces are still moving away from each other but the rate of separation is insufficient to sustain the cavity. The cavity, therefore, begins to collapse. Throughout the collapse phase the cavity maintains its circular shape. There is no visible effect or alteration occurring within the circular boundary, only the very regular continuous diminishing of the cavity diameter until the cavity completely disappears.

It is questionable whether the residual fluid inside the cavity forms a network of walls completely bridging the space between the two parallel plates. If separating walls do exist the cavity is made up of many irregular shaped voids. The residual fluid may, however, be clinging only to the surface of one or both of the parallel plates. The cavity would then consist of a single void with a circular boundary. Whether or not the total cavity is segmented is unimportant since the pressure in the residual fluid is equal to the pressure in the voids. This has been determined by observing the decay of a cavity. As the fluid boundary of the cavity moves radially inward, it absorbs the residual oil without in any way causing it to be disturbed. The fact that there is no disturbance as the fluid front passes through both the voids and residual fluid indicates that the pressure in the residual oil is equal to the pressure in the voids and justifies considering the total area inside the circular boundary as a single cavity.

THEORETICAL CONSIDERATIONS

Before venturing into a mathematical analysis of this phenomenon, it would be well to reflect a moment upon the pictures which have been obtained. In this way we may best recognize the physical nature of the cavity formation and define the problem areas which must be analyzed. As shown in the photographs of Fig. 7, there are three distinct periods of cavity growth. First there is a period of nucleation, a period when many small cavities are seen to form in an apparently random pattern over the film extent. Then there is an extremely interesting but complex growth phenomenon which is characterized by a fracturing of the advancing cavity front. During this growth phase many fern-like structures form and migrate radially outward. The final stage is one of coalescence, a single cavity being formed which then collapses.

How does this dynamic cavity structure form and what are the factors that govern its history? To construct a mathematical model of these cavities which would reflect all of the complex nature of their growth would be an extremely difficult task. The complications which arise stem from two sources, one being

mechanical and the other mathematical. We are initially faced with the problem
of determining the physical nature of the flows about the cavities and of establish-
ing differential equations which are meaningful in the light of the mechanics of
the system. The second problem, which has been discussed by BIRKHOFF (p. 102),
is related to the nature of the liquid-gas interface, this being a free boundary.
In this instance another boundary condition is required in addition to those
required by the more prevalent problem which has fixed boundaries. This additional condition is required to establish the spacial extent of the free cavity
boundary. Finally the differential equations and the boundary conditions assumed
must result in a boundary value problem that is well-set. Although the analysis

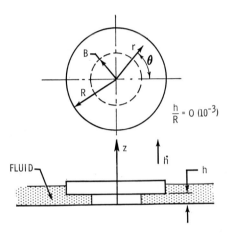

Fig. 8. Diagram of the coordinate system used for analyzing cavity growth.

of the complete system would be a formidable undertaking, and we suspect unjusti-
fied at this time, it would be of interest to investigate the problem in a somewhat
simplified form. We might suspect, for instance, that there exists some basic structure, relatively simple in nature, which accounts for the general behaviour pattern
of these cavities. With this thought in mind we will attempt to construct a well-
set problem, the solution of which will give us the dominant cavity growth pattern.

In Fig. 8 is shown a diagram of the system in which the cavity forms. It consists
of a circular disk of radius R which is maintained parallel to a fixed plane surface
and separated from it by a thickness $h(t)$. At time t_0 the gap width is h_0 and is
filled with a viscous liquid. With increasing time the two surfaces are pulled apart,
$\dot{h}(t) > 0$, and a circular cavity with radius $B(t)$ is formed. A cylindrical coordinate
system, r, θ, z, is used to define the cavity geometry. The fluid film thickness is
extremely small, the ratio of film thickness to disk radius being of the order of
10^{-3}.

Reference p. 137

ASSUMPTIONS

In this analysis, the following assumptions are made:
(a) the flow is laminar
(b) the viscosity μ is constant
(c) the fluid is incompressible
(d) there is no slip at the solid-liquid boundary
(e) the film thickness h is much less than the other dimensions of the system
(f) the effect of inertia terms, surface tension, and residual fluid in the cavity are negligible
(g) the cavity boundary is a single circle concentric with the disk.

Although the last assumption is not in accord with the observed initial cavity growth pattern, it is realistic for later stages of the cavity growth and on this basis will be retained in the initial analysis. It is possible to include first order approximations for the effects of inertia, surface tension, and residual oil in the analysis without causing undue mathematical hardships but their effects on the cavity formation are sufficiently small so that it appears advisable to discount them at this time.

Under these assumptions the problem becomes two dimensional in nature, a cavity forming whose geometry is that of a right circular cylinder with a time dependent radius and height. To preserve the two dimensional character of the flow, the cavity radius must always be greater than the film thickness. Consequently, at time zero it must be assumed that the cavity initially exists with $B_0 \gg h_0$. At the final instant of collapse as well as in the nucleation phase of cavity growth, factors which are not of a purely mechanistic nature undoubtedly influence the behaviour of the cavity. Although of interest, these effects are of a local character and have been omitted in this investigation of the gross features of the cavity formation.

ANALYSIS

The basic differential equations are obtained from the Navier-Stokes Equations and from the continuity equation by applying the usual thin film approximations (Ref. 1, Ch. 2). Because of the polar symmetry of the cavity, the basic equations reduce to the following forms,

$$\frac{dp}{dr} = \mu \frac{d^2u}{dz^2}, \qquad \frac{dp}{dz} = 0, \qquad \frac{dp}{d\theta} = 0, \qquad \frac{du}{dr} + \frac{u}{r} + \frac{dw}{dz} = 0. \qquad (1)$$

Since there is no slip at the solid surface, the following boundary conditions apply to the radial velocity u and the axial velocity w.

Reference p. 137

$$z = 0; \; u = 0 \text{ and } w = 0$$
$$z = h; \; u = 0 \text{ and } w = \dot{h} \qquad (2)$$

Under the assumption that the cavity pressure p_v is constant and that the pressure surrounding the disk is atmospheric p_a, then when $r = B$, $p = p_v$ and when $r = R$, $p = p_a$.

The pressure in the fluid film,

$$p = \frac{3\mu\dot{h}}{h^3} (r^2 - R^2) - \frac{\ln (r/R)}{\ln (B/R)} \left[p_a - p_v - \frac{3\mu\dot{h}}{h^3} (R^2 - B^2) \right] + p_a, \qquad (3)$$

is obtained by integrating eqns. (1) and utilizing the preceding boundary conditions.

The flow rate across any circumferential boundary can be expressed as $q = \bar{u}h$ where $\bar{u}$ is an average velocity. The flow rate q is obtained by integrating the radial velocity u over the film thickness. Thus,

$$\bar{u}h = \int_0^h u \, dz = \frac{-h^3}{12\mu} \left(\frac{dp}{dr} \right). \qquad (4)$$

At the cavity boundary, $r = B$ and the average velocity $\bar{u}$ is equal to the rate at which the cavity boundary is moving; thus $\bar{u} = \dot{B}$. From eqn. (4) we then obtain

$$\dot{B} = \frac{-h^2}{12\mu} \left(\frac{dp}{dr} \right)_B. \qquad (5)$$

It is interesting to observe that an expanding cavity, $\dot{B} > 0$, requires a negative pressure gradient along its boundary, a condition which characterizes a tension field about the cavity. Conversely a contracting cavity, $\dot{B} < 0$, requires a positive pressure gradient along its boundary and the fluid is in compression and flowing radially inward.

The pressure gradient at the cavity boundary is determined from both eqns. (5) and (3) and equating these expressions the following relationship is established,

$$\left(\frac{dp}{dr} \right)_B = \frac{-12\mu\dot{B}}{h^2} = \frac{6\mu\dot{h}B}{h^3} - \frac{1}{B \ln (B/R)} \left[p_a - p_v - \frac{3\mu\dot{h}}{h^3} (R^2 - B^2) \right]. \qquad (6)$$

From eqn. (6) we obtain a first order differential equation governing the time rate of change of the cavity radius as a function of known geometric and operational variables

$$\dot{B} = \frac{h^2}{12\mu B \ln (B/R)} \left[p_a - p_v - \frac{3\mu\dot{h}}{h^3} (R^2 - B^2) \right] - \frac{\dot{h}B}{2h}. \qquad (7)$$

To solve eqn. (7), it is necessary to know the analytical form of the time dependent film thickness $h(t)$. This is obtained from experimental data shown in Fig. 5 through a best fit approximation with a series of fifth degree polynomials. The second derivative of the resulting curve exists and is nowhere zero. Two of these curves are shown in Fig. 9. The initial film thickness is approximately 0.0002 inch and after 0.6 sec it is approximately 0.005 inch. It is within this extremely thin film that the cavity is initiated, grows, and finally collapses.

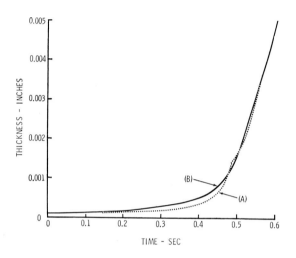

Fig. 9. The change with time of the film thickness h separating the two parallel surfaces.

Eqn. (7) is a first order differential equation which relates the cavity growth with time. The equation does not, however, indicate at what time a cavity should start to grow. Consequently, there is no indication as to when the integration of eqn. (7) should commence. But from Fig. 7, it is seen that there is no specific time when cavities form, instead they are initiated over a range of time. The time at which a particular cavity forms is a function of many factors which are not easily expressed in mathematical terms. These factors include such items as dissolved gases in the liquid, solid impurities contained in the fluid, small imperfections in the surfaces of the disk and plate resulting from machining operations, and minute quantities of undissolved gases which act as nucleation sites. Therefore, the initial time of cavity formation has been taken to be that instant when a small equivalent cavity is observed experimentally. Eqn. (7) is then integrated numerically using the Runge-Kutta-Gill method on a high speed digital computer.

Reference p. 137

RESULTS

The results of integrating eqn. (7) are seen in Figs. 10 and 11 which show the variation of the cavity radius with time. Although the initial portions of the experimental and calculated curves show a discrepancy, this is to be expected due to our assumption of circular symmetry for the cavity, a condition which is not fulfilled. However, during the latter portion of the time cycle, when experimental evidence supports the single cavity assumption, there is found an excellent

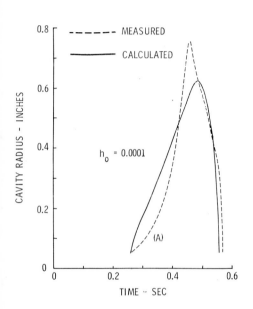

Fig. 10. The variation of cavity radius B, both measured and calculated, with respect to time.

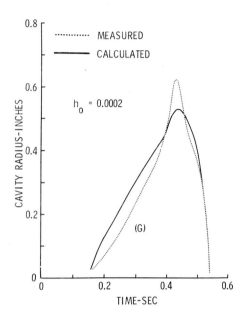

Fig. 11. The variation of cavity radius B, both measured and calculated, with respect to time.

correlation between theory and experiment. The difference in maximum cavity radius between the measured and calculated curves, although visually noticeable, is somewhat misleading. An earlier starting time for the numerical integrations results in a greater maximum value of the cavity radius without altering appreciably the collapse phase of the cavity history.

It is interesting to observe the theoretical pressure distributions across the fluid film at various times in the cavity growth. These are shown in Fig. 12 where the two curves which take on negative values are for an expanding cavity. When the cavity radius is maximum, the pressure derivative is zero at the cavity boundary and at succeeding times the pressure is always positive in the film as is shown by the other two curves in Fig. 12. The cavity is collapsing under these last two conditions and the fluid is flowing radially inward under the action of the positive pressure gradient.

In Fig. 13 is shown the velocity of the cavity boundary as a function of time.

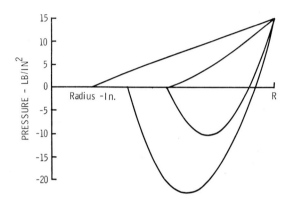

Fig. 12. Pressure distributions in the liquid film at different times. The curves with negative values are for an expanding cavity, the remaining curves are for a collapsing cavity.

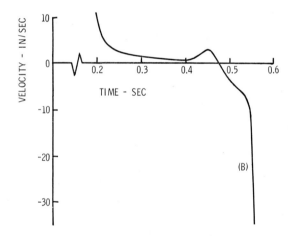

Fig. 13. The velocity of the cavity front, $\dot{B}$, versus time.

At the maximum velocity, which is approximately 35 inch/sec, the film thickness is 0.00325 inch and using the physical properties of the fluid, the Reynolds number is found to be approximately 7.0. This is sufficiently small to warrant the assumption of laminar flow in the system.

Reference p. 137

CONCLUSIONS

Within the framework of our assumptions it is possible to predict the general behaviour of a cavity formed between moving parallel plates. Since this is an initial endeavor toward the understanding of a complex phenomenon, it should not be expected to answer all questions nor should it reflect all of the complications and interactions observed experimentally. However, it has accomplished that which was desired, to see how closely a simplified analysis could come to predicting the cavity history. It is now time to refine the analysis so as to include more variables and to refine the experimental procedures so as to be able to measure the effects of these variables on the growth of such cavities.

REFERENCE

1 W. A. GROSS, *Gas Film Lubrication*, Wiley, New York, 1962.

Cavitation in Lubricating Oil Films

LEIF FLOBERG

Mechanical Engineering Department, Lund Institute of Technology, Lund, Sweden

Cavitation is a phenomenon which occurs in several different fields of nature. In modern technology the cavitation problem is becoming more and more important. In many machines fluids are subjected to pressure variations which give rise to cavitation. Some examples are the boat propeller, the water turbine, the journal bearing, and the fluid pump. Even human beings are subjected to cavitation. When flying, a rapid drop in the cabin pressure at a high altitude will give rise to cavitation in the blood. The same will happen to a diver who, after a deep dive, comes to the surface too fast. In some of the above cases cavitation must be avoided; in others the problem can be solved and necessary steps be taken.

In a bearing, which can be a plane pad bearing or a journal bearing, there is during perfect lubrication an oil film which completely separates the two sliding parts. Thus sliding in a correctly designed bearing will cause no wear. However, it is impossible to get the load carrying capacity without any power loss. The problem when designing a bearing is to choose the bearing dimensions, clearance, eccentricity, and oil viscosity so that the load will cause no wear, the power loss will be at a minimum, and there will be no overheating or vibration.

The basic theory of hydrodynamic lubrication was given by REYNOLDS[4] in 1886. He derived the equation for determining the pressure build-up in the oil film, and he was the first one to solve for the pressure build-up in a pad bearing and in a partial journal bearing both of infinite width. His theory is limited to full oil films of positive pressure and does not hold true when film rupture occurs due to cavitation.

Most authors who treat hydrodynamic lubrication show very little interest in cavitation zones in the bearings. Most of them neglect the ruptured part and make calculations for the positive pressure part based on arbitrarily chosen boundary conditions. Without studying the cavitation problem, it is not possible to tell which part of the bearing is the positive pressure part. In the literature the usual way to treat that problem is to solve Reynolds' equation as if negative pressures were possible, and then put all negative pressures equal to zero. This incorrect treatment of the problem is so frequent that it is worth a discussion.

Fig. 1 shows the oil film thickness for a journal bearing.

The surface speed is U. If, for the infinite bearing case, the pressure at $x = +\pi$ and $-\pi$—which is the same point—is set equal to zero, the pressure curve will be as shown in Fig. 2. If we now neglect the negative pressure curve, we get an incorrect solution, as the initial assumption of a full oil film all around the circum-

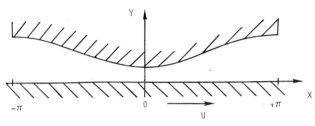

Fig. 1. Oil film thickness.

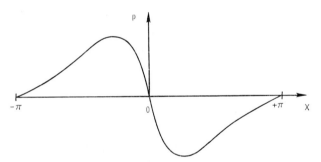

Fig. 2. Pressure curve.

ference then is no longer valid. After the solution is obtained, it is not possible to change the assumptions on which the solution is based. However, the solution is correct for the 180° partial journal bearing case.

Let us study now the oil flow at $x = 0$. In the oil region just to the left of $x = 0$ the oil flow consists of two parts, see Fig. 3. The surface velocity gives rise to a linear velocity distribution, Fig. 3a, and the pressure gradient gives a parabolic distribution, Fig. 3b. The total velocity distribution for the end of the pressure build-up is shown in Fig. 3c. If a cavitation region with constant pressure should start at $x = 0$ and end at $x = \pi$, the oil flow just to the right of $x = 0$ would be represented by the velocity distribution in Fig. 3a. An oil flow corresponding to that in Fig. 3b would then vanish in space just at the point $x = 0$. The continuity condition is thus not fulfilled and the solution must be rejected. This example gives a good view of the problem which has to be solved.

In a cavitation region the pressure is constant and equal to the cavitation pressure. The vapor pressure of an ideal oil is very close to an absolute vacuum. However, gases dissolved in the oil are released at a higher pressure than the vapor pressure. The value of the cavitation pressure must be experimentally determined. Experiments show that fluids dissolve gases in proportion to the pressure. The higher the pressure, the more gas there is in the fluid. When the

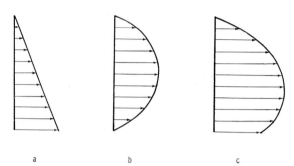

Fig. 3. Oil flow velocity distributions.

pressure is increased air or gas goes into the fluid and when the pressure is decreased it comes out. The cavitation pressure is thus equal to that pressure at which the fluid is in contact with air or gas. It could be 10 atmospheres gauge or it could be atmospheric pressure.

Let us now study a cavitation region in a lubricating oil film, starting with the two-dimensional case. In this case there are no velocities in the axial direction and the pressure is constant within the cavitation region and equal to the cavitation pressure. To determine the pressure curve at a given eccentricity, one boundary condition is needed. Let us study the continuity of flow at the boundaries of the ruptured zone. At the end of the pressure build-up the oil flow per unit width is

$$q_{oil} = \frac{Uh}{2} - \frac{h^3}{12\eta} \cdot \frac{dp}{dx}$$

in which

h = oil film thickness
η = oil viscosity.

The flow entering the cavitation region is

$$q_{cav} = \theta \cdot \frac{Uh}{2}$$

in which $0 \leq \theta \leq 1$, because it is not certain that the oil fills up all the width. These two expressions must be equal and

$$(1 - \theta)\, \frac{Uh}{2} - \frac{h^3}{12\eta} \cdot \frac{\mathrm{d}p}{\mathrm{d}x} = 0 \,.$$

As there are no pressures lower than the cavitation pressure, $\mathrm{d}p/\mathrm{d}x$ cannot be positive but must be negative or zero. Then the solution of the equation is

$$\frac{\mathrm{d}p}{\mathrm{d}x} = 0$$

$$\theta = 1.$$

The last condition means that the oil will fill all the width at the start of cavitation. Depending on adhesion and cohesion forces of the oil, it will divide into streamlets, whose behaviour can easily be experimentally determined. Fig. 4 shows a pressure

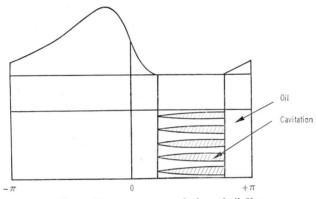

Fig. 4. Pressure curve and view of oil film.

curve determined from the condition $\mathrm{d}p/\mathrm{d}x = 0$ at the start of cavitation and gives the behaviour of the oil. At the start of pressure build-up, there will be a jump in the pressure derivative. The continuity condition is automatically satisfied at this point because Reynolds' equation is satisfied in the oil film region. The break in the pressure curve is the same sort of break as occurs in the ambient pressure curve at the surface of a lake—a break caused by the difference in density between air and water. In a bearing the break is caused by the difference between the viscosities of gas and oil. The shape of the pressure curve depends on the boundary condition. There are an infinite number of curves. The two extreme bounding curves between which all these other curves lie are: (I) the curve shown above in Fig. 2—which is based on a full oil film all around the circumference— modified by placing an oil-groove with cavitation pressure at the minimum

References p. 146

pressure point; and (II) the constant pressure distribution—with a cavitation region all around the circumference—that is obtained when an oil groove with cavitation pressure is located at the minimum oil film thickness. To the full oil film solution (I) any constant pressure can be added.

Let us study now the three-dimensional case, starting with the pressure determination in the oil region. The pressure is determined from Reynolds' equation

$$\frac{\partial}{\partial x}\left(\frac{h^3}{\eta}\cdot\frac{\partial p}{\partial x}\right) + \frac{\partial}{\partial z}\left(\frac{h^3}{\eta}\cdot\frac{\partial p}{\partial z}\right) = 6U\cdot\frac{\partial h}{\partial x}$$

in which z is the coordinate in the axial direction.

The viscosity η is a function of the pressure p and the temperature t. The temperature is derived from the energy equation

$$\left[\frac{Uh}{2} - \frac{h^3}{12\eta}\cdot\frac{\partial p}{\partial x}\right]c\varrho\cdot\frac{\partial t}{\partial x} - \frac{h^3}{12\eta}\cdot\frac{\partial p}{\partial z}\cdot c\varrho\cdot\frac{\partial t}{\partial z} - \frac{h^3}{12\eta}\left[\left(\frac{\partial p}{\partial x}\right)^2 + \left(\frac{\partial p}{\partial z}\right)^2\right] - \frac{\eta U^2}{h} = 0$$

in which

$$c = \text{specific heat of oil}$$
$$\varrho = \text{density of oil.}$$

When determining the pressure build-up in a finite bearing, there are certain boundary conditions which have to be satisfied. If the solution of the equations

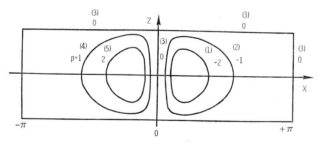

Fig. 5. Pressure field.

gives a pressure distribution that is everywhere positive, which means that it is higher than the cavitation pressure, the solution is a valid one; if negative pressures appear, cavitation occurs and the solution must be rejected. For the classical analysis of a grooveless bearing, if the boundary pressure is equal to zero, the pressure solution looks like that in Fig. 5. In the converging part of the bearing, the pressures will be positive; in the diverging part, negative. Any constant pressure can be added to each of the pressures in Fig. 5 giving a new theoretical solution that satisfies different boundary conditions. The new solution is physically valid if all pressures are higher than the cavitation pressure; if that is not the case,

References p. 146

the solution must be rejected. The figures within parentheses in Fig. 5 show the
new pressure distribution that is obtained when a constant pressure of 3 is added;
the new solution is valid.

Let us study now the continuity conditions at the boundary of a cavitation
region. This study must be split into two parts—one part for the upstream boundary and the other for the downstream boundary of the region. An arbitrary cavitation region is shown in Fig. 6, where a strip of the width Δz is cut out. The oil flow

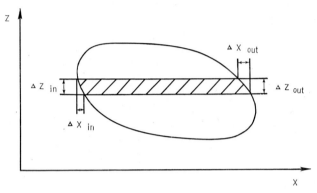

Fig. 6. Cavitation region.

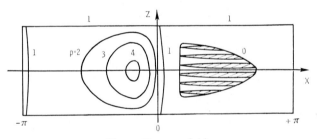

Fig. 7. Pressure field.

entering the cavitation region over the strip width $\Delta z_{in} = \Delta z_{out} = \Delta z$ is for the
oil region

$$\Delta Q_{oil} = \left[\frac{Uh}{2} - \frac{h^3}{12\eta} \cdot \frac{\partial p}{\partial x}\right] \Delta z_{in} - \frac{h^3}{12\eta} \cdot \frac{\partial p}{\partial z} \cdot \Delta x_{in}$$

and for the cavitation region as above

$$\Delta Q_{cav} = \theta \cdot \frac{Uh}{2} \cdot \Delta z_{in}$$

in which $0 \leq \theta \leq 1$.

References p. 146

Fig. 8. Photos of a cavitation region.

Fig. 9. Photo of a cavitation region.

The continuity condition gives

$$(\mathrm{I} - \theta)\,\frac{Uh}{2}\cdot \Delta z_{\mathrm{in}} - \frac{h^3}{12\eta}\cdot\frac{\partial p}{\partial x}\cdot \Delta z_{\mathrm{in}} - \frac{h^3}{12\eta}\cdot\frac{\partial p}{\partial z}\cdot \Delta x_{\mathrm{in}} = 0.$$

As the cavitation pressure is the lowest pressure in the bearing, $\partial p/\partial x$ and $\partial p/\partial z$ must be negative or zero. We have the sum of three non-negative terms equal to zero, hence each term must be zero. Thus

$$\frac{\partial p}{\partial x} = \frac{\partial p}{\partial z} = 0 \qquad\qquad \theta = \mathrm{I}$$

which condition holds for the upstream part of the cavitation region. At the start of cavitation the oil fills the entire width and the various directional derivatives of the pressure are zero.

In the cavitation region the oil divides into streamlets. Since there the pressure is constant, there is no flow of oil in the axial direction. Thus the oil flow entering the region over the strip width Δz_{in} in Fig. 6 must leave over the same width Δz_{out} at the downstream boundary. The flow within the cavitation region over the strip width Δz is

References p. 146

$$\Delta Q_{cav} = \frac{U h_{in}}{2} \cdot \Delta z_{in}$$

and the flow entering the oil region over the same width is

$$\Delta Q_{oil} = \frac{U h_{out}}{2} \cdot \Delta z_{out} - \frac{h_{out}^3}{12 \eta_{out}} \left[\frac{\partial p}{\partial x} \cdot \Delta z_{out} + \frac{\partial p}{\partial z} \cdot \Delta x_{out} \right] .$$

These two expressions must be equal and when $\Delta z \to 0$ we have

$$\frac{U h_{in}}{2} = \frac{U h_{out}}{2} - \frac{h_{out}^3}{12 \eta_{out}} \left[\frac{\partial p}{\partial x} - \frac{\partial p}{\partial z} \cdot \frac{dx}{dz} \right]$$

which is the continuity condition at the downstream boundary of the cavitation region. The temperature rise through the cavitation region is determined by

$$\frac{\partial t}{\partial x} = \frac{2U}{c\varrho} \cdot \frac{\eta}{h^2} .$$

A pressure field with a cavitation region derived from the equations and conditions given above is shown in Fig. 7. Two photos of cavitation regions are shown in Figs. 8 and 9. Fig. 8 represents a journal bearing and Fig. 9 a cylinder rotating on a plane surface. Experimental investigations of cavitation regions are given in Refs. 1, 2, and 3.

REFERENCES

1 L. FLOBERG, Lubrication of Two Cylindrical Surfaces, Considering Cavitation, *Trans. Chalmers Univ. Technol. (Gothenburg)*, No. 234, 1961.
2 L. FLOBERG, Experimental Investigation of Cavitation Regions in Journal Bearings, *Trans. Chalmers Univ. Technol. (Gothenburg)*, No. 238, 1961.
3 L. FLOBERG, On Hydrodynamic Lubrication with Special Reference to Cavitation in Bearings, *Dissertations Chalmers Univ. Technol. (Gothenburg)*, No. 30, 1961.
4 O. REYNOLDS, On the Theory of Lubrication, *Phil. Trans. Roy. Soc. London*, 177 (1886) 157.

The Molecular Theory of Surface Tension

I. PRIGOGINE[*]

*Faculté des Sciences,
University of Brussels, Brussels, Belgium*

I. INTRODUCTION

The surface tension σ of a liquid is one of the most fundamental quantities which appears in cavitation problems. It determines both the mechanical equilibrium of the cavity

$$p'' - p' = \frac{2\sigma}{r} \qquad \text{(Laplace equation)}$$

and the kinetics of formation of microscopic cavities[1]. The macroscopic meaning of surface tension and more generally the thermodynamics of surfaces is now well understood. However the situation is not so favorable in respect to the molecular theory of surface tension. This is a much more complex subject which belongs to equilibrium statistical mechanics. This field has progressed in an amazing way in the last twenty years, but still much remains to be done.

The object of this lecture is to present a short summary of the present day application of statistical mechanics to surface tension. My main concern will be to present a short physical description of the basic methods used and to discuss their results and their limitations. For obvious reasons we shall limit ourselves to classical systems for which quantum mechanical effects play no essential role[**].

2. THE TOOLS OF EQUILIBRIUM STATISTICAL MECHANICS[***]

a) One of the central quantities of equilibrium statistical mechanics is the *partition function*

$$Z = \sum_r e^{-\beta E_r} \qquad (2.1)$$

with

---

[*] Visiting Consultant to the General Motors Research Laboratories.
[**] For an excellent short account of quantum mechanical effects see HARASIMA[19].
[***] For more details see any textbook of statistical mechanics, *e.g.* Refs. 2, 3.

References p. 162–163

$$\beta = (kT)^{-1} \tag{2.2}$$

where k is Boltzmann's constant and T the absolute temperature. It is a weighted sum over all energy levels of the system. The partition function is closely related to the Helmholtz free energy F. It may be shown that

$$F = - kT \lg Z \tag{2.3}$$

In the classical limit (2.1) can be expressed as the multiple integral (taking only account of translational motion)

$$Z = \frac{1}{N!} \frac{1}{h^{3N}} \int \cdots \int e^{-\beta H} \, d\mathbf{p}_1 \cdots d\mathbf{p}_N \, d\mathbf{r}_1 \cdots d\mathbf{r}_N \tag{2.4}$$

Here H is the hamiltonian of the system which is generally of the form

$$H = \frac{1}{2m} \sum_{i=1}^{N} (\mathbf{p}_i)^2 + \sum_{i<j}^{N} \varepsilon(r_{ij}) \tag{2.5}$$

where $\varepsilon(r_{ij})$ is the interaction energy between molecules i and j. Also N is the number of particles and h Planck's constant. If (2.5) is introduced into (2.4) Z splits into a product of two factors due respectively to the kinetic energy and the potential energy. The first factor is readily found to be

$$\left[\frac{1}{h} (2\pi m kT)^{\frac{1}{2}} \right]^{3N} \tag{2.6}$$

It depends only on the temperature and not on the density and plays no role in the problems we shall study here. The second factor is

$$Q = \frac{1}{N!} \int \cdots \int e^{-\beta \sum \varepsilon_{ij}} \, d\mathbf{r}_1 \cdots d\mathbf{r}_N \tag{2.7}$$

It is often called the *configurational partition function*.

The integration extends over the volume V of the system. For example for a perfect gas ($\varepsilon_{ij} = 0$)

$$Q = \frac{1}{N!} \int \cdots \int d\mathbf{r}_1 \cdots d\mathbf{r}_N = \frac{V^N}{N!} \tag{2.8}$$

The evaluation of the multiple integral (2.7) is the central problem of equilibrium statistical mechanics. Unfortunately only for a few special models has such an evaluation been proved possible till now (for example one-dimensional models corresponding to N particles on a line). In other cases one is forced to introduce *a priori* simplifications (as for example in the cell model of liquids, see section 3) or to use perturbation techniques. Completely new mathematical techniques are badly needed.

References p. 162–163

b) a second basic tool of equilibrium statistical mechanics is *molecular distribution functions*.

By definition

$$n^{(h)}(\mathbf{r}_1 \ldots \mathbf{r}_h) \, d\mathbf{r}_1 \ldots d\mathbf{r}_h \qquad (2.9)$$

gives the probability of finding simultaneously h molecules at positions $\mathbf{r}_1$, $\mathbf{r}_2$, ..., $\mathbf{r}_h$.

The most important distribution functions are $n^{(1)}(\mathbf{r})$ which is just the number density and $n^{(2)}(\mathbf{r}_1, \mathbf{r}_2)$. For sufficiently large uniform systems the number density may be considered as constant

$$n^{(1)} = \frac{N}{V} = C \qquad (2.10)$$

The quantity $n^{(2)}(\mathbf{r}_1, \mathbf{r}_2) \, d\mathbf{r}_1 d\mathbf{r}_2$ gives the probability that there is a molecule in the volume element $d\mathbf{r}_1$ about $\mathbf{r}_1$ and simultaneously a molecule in $d\mathbf{r}_2$ about $\mathbf{r}_2$. This is of course no more so in the transition region between liquid and vapor.

The importance of $n^{(1)}$ and $n^{(2)}$ comes from the fact that it is possible to express many fundamental thermodynamic and hydrodynamic quantities in terms of them. For example, the stress tensor $P_{ij}(\mathbf{r})$ at the point $\mathbf{r}$ may be expressed by[4]

$$P_{ij}(\mathbf{r}) = \underline{k}Tn_1(\mathbf{r}) \, \delta_{ij} - \tfrac{1}{2} \int d\mathbf{R} \, \frac{R_i R_j}{|\mathbf{R}|} \, \varepsilon'(R) n_2(\mathbf{r}, \mathbf{r} + \mathbf{R}) \qquad (2.11)$$

It appears as the sum of two contributions: a kinetic term due to thermal motion and a potential term due to the interactions between molecules.

While a formal expression involving the distribution functions may readily be established, the evaluation of the distribution function in terms of intermolecular forces is a problem of comparable difficulty as the evaluation of the partition function.

c) Because it is difficult to achieve an *a priori* evaluation of the partition function or of the distribution functions, it is important to use, as fully as possible, arguments based on the dimensions of the physical quantities involved.

Now very often a satisfactory approximation for the potential energy of a pair of molecules $\varepsilon(r)$ is provided by the expression

$$\varepsilon(r) = \varepsilon^\times \varphi(r/r^\times) \qquad (2.12)$$

where φ is some universal function, $\varepsilon^\times$ and $r^\times$ being two scale factors characteristic of the molecular species. A useful approximation is the so-called (6–12) law of Lennard-Jones

$$\varphi(r/r^\times) = -2(r^\times/r)^6 + (r^\times/r)^{12} \qquad (2.13)$$

The scale factors $\varepsilon^\times$, $r^\times$ have then a simple meaning: they represent the coordinates of the minimum of $\varepsilon(r)$.

This law applies to monoatomic molecules like He, A, Kr and with some reservations, to rather spherical molecules like CCl_4, $C(CH_3)_4$, H_2, N_2.... If we introduce (2.12) into (2.7) we obtain

$$Q = (r^\times)^{3N}[q(\tilde{T}, \tilde{v})]^N \tag{2.14}$$

where $\tilde{T}$, $\tilde{v}$ are the reduced variables

$$\tilde{T} = \frac{kT}{\varepsilon^\times}, \qquad \tilde{v} = \frac{v}{(r^\times)^3} \tag{2.15'}$$

We also define the reduced pressure

$$\tilde{p} = p(r^\times)^3/\varepsilon^\times \tag{2.15''}$$

Using (2.14) and the relation (2.3) between partition function and free energy we obtain the equation of state

$$\tilde{p} = \tilde{p}(\tilde{T}, \tilde{v}) \tag{2.16}$$

This equation expresses the theorem of corresponding states. The important point is that the reduced variables (2.15) are defined in terms of the macroscopic variables T, v, p and molecular parameters. This will prove important later (see section 8).

After this brief review of the main tools of equilibrium statistical mechanics, let us consider their application to the problem of surface tensions.

3. THEOREM OF CORRESPONDING STATES

Using the scale factors $\varepsilon^\times$, $r^\times$ defined in section 2 we may define the reduced surface tension

$$\tilde{\sigma} = \frac{\sigma(r^\times)^2}{\varepsilon^\times} = \tilde{\sigma}(\tilde{T}) \tag{3.1}$$

which is a universal function of the reduced temperature $\tilde{T}$ (see 2.15). In the domain of validity of the theorem of corresponding states we have

$$\varepsilon^\times \sim T_c, \qquad (r^\times)^3 \sim v_c \tag{3.2}$$

where T_c, v_c are respectively the critical temperature and the critical volume. We may therefore also write (3.1) in the form

$$\sigma = T_c v_c^{-2/3} f(T/T_c). \tag{3.3}$$

GUGGENHEIM[5] has proposed the following empirical expression for $f(T/T_c)$:

$$f(T/T_c) = 4.4 \, (1 - T/T_c)^{11/9} \text{ ergs deg}^{-1} \text{ mole}^{-2\,3}. \tag{3.4}$$

Guggenheim has also shown that

$$\frac{\sigma^{3/11}}{v_L^{-1} - v_g^{-1}} = \text{constant} \tag{3.5}$$

where v_L, v_g are the molar volume of the liquid and the gas. This is a modification of earlier formulae by Kleeman and Mac Leod (see Ref. 5 for the references).

We shall come back to the theoretical justification of (3.4) and (3.5).

4. CELL MODEL

Two general methods can be used to express the surface tension in terms of inter-molecular forces. The first is based on the partition function formalism, the second on the distribution functions.

The link with the partition function is simple. We have indeed the thermo-dynamical expression[1]

$$\sigma = \left(\frac{\partial F}{\partial \Omega} \right)_{VTN} \tag{4.1}$$

and we have seen that the free energy F is related directly to the partition function by formula (2.3).

In this section we shall consider a simple model for the partition function which leads to a semiquantitative description of the surface tension. In section 7 we shall discuss a more rigorous direction of approach. The model we shall consider here is the so-called cell model (or free volume theory) for pure liquids (for more details, see Ref. 3).

For densities as high as these in the solid state and in the liquid state far below the critical temperature, we may expect a certain order in the mutual distribution of the molecules. Intermolecular distances between first neighbours smaller than the molecular diameter σ are prohibited by the strong repulsive forces, while distances much larger are statistically very unlikely. This introduces a regularity in the spacing of neighbouring molecules with a mean intermolecular distance of the order of the molecular diameter. This more or less regular structure forms the basis of the cell model in its simplest form: it is assumed that each molecule is confined to its own cell.

Let us call Ψ the partition function corresponding to a molecule in its cell referred to the particle at the center of its cell. We assume that the mean energy of interaction with neighbouring particles $\omega(r)$ depends only on the distance of the

References p. 162–163

molecule from the center of the cell. Thus we have for the cell partition function

$$\Psi = 4\pi \int_{\text{cell}} \exp\left[-\beta(\omega(r) - \omega(0))\right] r^2 \, dr \tag{4.2}$$

where $\omega(0)$ is the value of $\omega(r)$ at the center of the cell. The partition function Q of the system of N particles may now be written in the form

$$Q = \Psi^N \exp\left[-\tfrac{1}{2}\beta N\omega(0)\right] \tag{4.3}$$

The mean energy of interaction $\omega(r)$ can easily be estimated from the interaction $\varepsilon(r)$ between the molecules. The corresponding free energy is

$$F = N\left\{\tfrac{1}{2}\omega(0) - kT \lg \Psi - \tfrac{3}{2}kT \lg \frac{2\pi mkT}{h^2}\right\} \tag{4.4}$$

Let us now extend this model to include surface phenomena[6,7,8]. We imagine the liquid subdivided into monomolecular layers containing each N_c lattice sites. Each molecule has z first neighbours: lz in the same layer and mz in each of the adjacent layers. We have, therefore:

$$l + 2m = 1 \tag{4.5}$$

For example, for a simple cubic lattice $l = \tfrac{2}{3}$, $m = \tfrac{1}{6}$. We first assume that all lattice sites are occupied.

The molecules which form the surface layer are clearly submitted to a different average potential both because of the lack of symmetry and because of the decrease in the number of first neighbours which is $(l + m)z$. Let us call Ψ' and $\omega'(0)$ the cell partition functions and the value of the average potential for the molecules in the surface layer.

The trivial extension of (4.3) is then

$$Q = \Psi^{N-N_c} (\Psi')^{N_c} e^{-\frac{1}{2}\frac{(N-N_c)\omega(0) + N_c\omega'(0)}{kT}} \tag{4.6}$$

The corresponding free energy is

$$F = N\left\{\tfrac{1}{2}\omega(0) - kT \lg \Psi - \tfrac{3}{2}kT \lg \frac{2\pi mkT}{h^2}\right\}$$
$$+ N_c\left\{\tfrac{1}{2}[\omega'(0) - \omega(0)] - kT \lg \frac{\Psi'}{\Psi}\right\} \tag{4.7}$$

The second term corresponds to the *excess free energy* introduced by the surface. The surface area is related to N_c by

$$\Omega = N_c\omega \tag{4.8}$$

and (4.7) gives us therefore the simple expression for the surface tension

$$\sigma\omega = \tfrac{1}{2}[\omega'(0) - \omega(0)] - \underline{k}T \lg \frac{\Psi'}{\Psi} \tag{4.9}$$

as well as for the surface energy and the surface entropy

$$e^{\mathrm{a}}\omega = \tfrac{1}{2}[\omega'(0) - \omega(0)] + \underline{k}T^2 \frac{\partial}{\partial T} \lg \frac{\Psi'}{\Psi} \tag{4.10}$$

$$s^{\mathrm{a}}\omega = \underline{k} \lg \frac{\Psi'}{\Psi} + \underline{k}T \frac{\partial}{\partial T} \lg \frac{\Psi'}{\Psi} \tag{4.11}$$

Whenever the molecular interaction laws are known it is easy to give a numerical estimate based on formulas (4.9)–(4.11) (see Ref. 8). The results for argon at 85° K are summarized in Table I.

TABLE I

SURFACE PROPERTIES OF ARGON AT 85° K[8]

	σ	e^{a}	s^{a}
	erg cm^{-2}	*erg cm*$^{-2}$	*erg cm*$^{-2}$ *deg*$^{-1}$
Observed	13.2	35.3	0.26
Calculated	9.0	25.8	0.17
Calculated with correction due to holes	13.0	37.3	0.27

Similar results have been obtained for many substances. The agreement is good for the surface tension but less good for the surface entropy (or energy). The surface is much more disordered than assumed by the quasi-crystalline model we have used. A rough correction can be introduced by assuming that some lattice sites are empty (see Refs. 8, 9). The number of such 'holes' is adjusted to minimize the free energy. This changes a little the surface tension but improves much the agreement for the surface entropy and energy.

However, it is clear that this 'hole model' is an over-simplification. We meet here the basic difficulty which prevents us from developing a really quantitative theory of liquids. The next approximation after the one-particle cell model should take account of *density fluctuations* which may be expected to become specially important in the surface layer. But still no quantitative formulation of such a theory is available in spite of many efforts (for more details, see Ref. 3).

5. SURFACE PHENOMENA AND DISTRIBUTION FUNCTIONS

Instead of starting with the partition function formalism combined with the thermodynamic formula (4.1), we may also express directly the surface tension in terms of the molecular distribution function introduced in section 2. A general proof that the two approaches are rigorously equivalent has been given by BUFF[10].

It is indeed known since the classical work of Van der Waals, Bakker and others that the surface tension may be expressed in terms of the variation of the *tangential component of the pressure tensor in the surface layer*. If we combine this with the expression (2.11) of the pressure tensor we obtain the Kirkwood-Buff formula[11]

$$\sigma = \frac{1}{2} \int_0^\infty dz \int \frac{d\varepsilon}{dR} \frac{(x_2 - x_1)^2}{R} [n^{(2)}(z_1, \mathbf{R}) - n_g^{(2)}(R)] \, d\mathbf{R} +$$

$$+ \frac{1}{2} \int_{-\infty}^0 dz \int \frac{d\varepsilon}{dR} \frac{(x_2 - x_1)^2}{R} [n^{(2)}(z_1, \mathbf{R}) - n_L^{(2)}(R)] \, d\mathbf{R} \tag{5.1}$$

Here z is the direction normal to the phase separation surface. The surface corresponding to zero absorption is situated at $z = 0$. The two-particle distribution functions $n_g^{(2)}$ and $n_L^{(2)}$ correspond respectively to the homogeneous gas and liquid phases.

This formula is still rigorous, but unfortunately we do not know the exact form of the two particle distribution function in the transition zone. To obtain a numerical estimate Kirkwood and Buff make the following simplifying assumptions:

a) the gas is infinitely dilute;

b) the liquid is homogeneous till the surface of phase separation.

Then (5.1) reduces to the expression (which had also been derived by FOWLER[21])

$$\sigma = \frac{\pi}{8} \int_0^\infty \frac{d\varepsilon(R)}{dR} R^4 n_L^{(2)}(R) \, dR \tag{5.2}$$

A numerical estimate gave for argon at 90° K, 14.9 dyn/cm, in reasonable agreement with the experimental value 11.9.

However it is clear that this model corresponds again to a crude oversimplification. As shown by HARASIMA[19] the variation of the pressure tensor itself in the transition region is even qualitatively incorrectly described in this model.

6. MULTIPLE LAYER MODEL

In both methods we have summarized, the starting point is rigorous but one is forced to introduce drastic approximations at a later stage. However in my opinion the cell model has the advantage of greater simplicity which in turn permits one to introduce, when necessary, supplementary physical refinements.

For example, a calculation similar to that of section 4 may be performed to calculate the interfacial tension at the surface between two partially miscible liquids. Let us call T_c the critical temperature of mixing. One then obtains[1, 12]

$$\sigma = \frac{6mkT_c}{\omega} \left(\frac{T_c}{T} - 1 \right) \qquad (6.1)$$

where m has been defined in (4.5) and ω is the area per molecule.

To derive this expression it has been assumed that the surface phase may be adequately described by a monolayer sandwiched between the two homogeneous phases*:

phase one

---

monolayer

---

phase two

Formula (6.1) implies a linear variation of the surface tension near the critical temperature in contradiction with the thermodynamic requirement that the surface entropy vanishes

$$\left(\frac{d\sigma}{dT} \right)_{T \to T_c} \to 0 \qquad (6.2)$$

at the critical temperature because the two phases become identical. Indeed the careful experimental investigation of ATACK AND RICE[13] gives for the surface tension near the critical point for the mixtures cyclohexane-aniline the following expression

$$\log_{10}\sigma = 1.80 + 1.39 \log_{10} (1 - T/T_c) \qquad (6.3)$$

As has been shown by COHEN AND HILLIARD[14] as well as by BELLEMANS[15] this contradiction disappears when a multiple layer model for the surface tension is used. Below $0.9\ T/T_c$ the monolayer model remains correct but above this temperature the width of the transition region increases rapidly and near the critical point a continuous description is therefore much more appropriate. The surface tension then takes the following remarkable form:

$$\sigma = 4m \frac{kT_c}{\omega} \int_{-\infty}^{+\infty} \left(\frac{dx(z)}{dz} \right)^2 dz \qquad (6.4)$$

where $x(z)$ is the mole fraction considered as a function of the position z in the layer. The surface tension is then proportional to the square of the gradient of the mole fraction integrated over the whole surface region. This gives the expression

$$\sigma = 2\sqrt{2m} \frac{kT_c}{\omega} \left(1 - \frac{T}{T_c} \right)^{3/2} \qquad (6.5)$$

---

* Moreover in this calculation the theory of strictly regular solutions is used. The characteristic feature of this theory is that the chemical potentials are very simple functions of the mole fractions (see Ref. 3 or 20 for more details).

Instead of a linear variation we now have $\sigma \sim (1 - T/T_c)^{3/2}$. When applied to the cyclohexane-aniline mixtures this expression gives[15]

$$\log_{10} \sigma = 1.25 + 1.50 \log_{10} (1 - T/T_c) \tag{6.6}$$

The temperature variation is correctly described. No quantitative agreement may be expected because the strong dipolar interactions between aniline molecules are not taken into account in this model.

However the continuum model can only be used near the critical point. At low temperature it introduces thermodynamic contradictions (see Ref. 15) and the monolayer model is then correct.

With minor alterations similar calculations using a multiple layer model may be made for the liquid vapor surface[9, 15], one of molecular species being now replaced by 'holes'. Formula (6.5)

$$\sigma \sim (T_c - T)^{3/2} \tag{6.7}$$

has to be compared with the empirical formula (see 3.4)

$$\sigma \sim (T_c - T)^{11/9} \tag{6.8}$$

Also this model predicts

$$\frac{\sigma^{1/3}}{v_L^{-1} - v_g^{-1}} = \text{constant} \tag{6.9}$$

in satisfactory agreement with the empirical Mac Leod-Guggenheim formula (3.5).

7. CLUSTER EXPANSION METHODS

Is it not possible to avoid any *a priori* assumption about the surface layer and to obtain at least some exact result? This is the direction which has been explored in the recent important work by BELLEMANS[16] as well as by STILLINGER AND BUFF[17]. Bellemans' papers are more specially devoted to surface phenomena while the formalism of Stillinger and Buff is more general. For this reason Bellemans obtains more detailed results concerning surface phenomena, and we shall follow his methods here. But in both papers the idea is the same: surface phenomena may be treated by extending the usual methods of statistical mechanics to include the effect of external fields.

To understand this method let us go back to the expression (2.7) of the configurational partition function. While it has not yet been possible to find a compact expression for (2.7) it is always possible to obtain an expansion in terms of powers of the concentration. This is the so-called Ursell-Mayer expansion (see for example Ref. 2). One first introduces the 'f-functions' defined by

$$f = e^{-\frac{\varepsilon}{kT}} - 1 \qquad (7.1)$$

which differ from zero only for two molecules in interaction (then $\varepsilon \neq 0$). Such a couple of molecules say i and j in interaction is represented by a 'bond'.

$$(7.2)$$

If (7.1) is introduced into (2.7) we obtain

$$Q = \frac{1}{N!} \int \cdots \int \prod_{i<j} (1 + f_{ij}) \, d\mathbf{r_1} \cdots d\mathbf{r_N} \qquad (7.3)$$

After rather lengthy manipulations a concentration expansion for the pressure may be deduced:

$$p = CkT[1 - \sum_{k=1}^{\infty} k\beta_k C^k/(k+1)] \qquad (7.4)$$

Here the β_k are the so-called *irreducible cluster integrals*. They correspond to contributions of $k + 1$ molecules forming multiply connected bond patterns. For example

$$1!\beta_1 = \quad = \int d\mathbf{r_2} f_{12}$$

$$2!\beta_2 = \quad = \int d\mathbf{r_2} \, d\mathbf{r_3} \, f_{12} f_{23} f_{31} \qquad (7.5)$$

Let us consider the case of hard spheres. Then

$$\begin{aligned} f &= -1 \quad \text{if} \quad r < D \\ &= 0 \quad \text{if} \quad r \geq D \end{aligned} \qquad (7.6)$$

where D is the radius. It should be noticed that the whole contribution to the cluster integrals comes from regions where at least two hard spheres are overlapping.

The formula (7.4) expresses one of the most beautiful results of equilibrium statistical mechanics. As shown by (7.5) each of the coefficients in the expansion has a simple topological meaning. For example, the coefficient of C^3 is expressed only in terms of the three body interaction represented by a triangular bond.

A somewhat similar expansion is valid for solutions[2]; C is then the concentration of the solute.

References p. 162–163

Let us now go back to Bellemans' method for the evaluation of surface properties. Bellemans considers N particles enclosed in a given volume V bounded by an external surface Ω. Outside this volume the concentration is assumed to be zero. This introduces supplementary surface dependent contribution to the cluster integrals. Let us, for example, consider the integral (see eqn. (7.5))

$$\int_V d\mathbf{r}_1 \int_V d\mathbf{r}_2 \, f_{12} \tag{7.7}$$

and introduce the function Δ_2 related to the second molecule such that

$$\begin{aligned}
\Delta_2 &= 1 \quad \text{if } 2 \quad \text{inside } V \\
&= 0 \quad\quad\quad \text{outside } V
\end{aligned} \tag{7.8}$$

We then have (we assume a plane surface situated at $z = 0$)

$$\begin{aligned}
\int_V d\mathbf{r}_1 \int_V d\mathbf{r}_2 \, f_{12} &= \int_V d\mathbf{r}_1 \int_\infty d\mathbf{r}_2 \, f_{12} \, \Delta_2 \\
&= \int_V d\mathbf{r}_1 \int_\infty d\mathbf{r}_2 \, f_{12} + \int_V d\mathbf{r}_1 \int_\infty d\mathbf{r}_2 \, f_{12} \, (\Delta_2 - 1) \\
&= V\beta_1 + \Omega \int_0^\infty dz_2 \int_V d\mathbf{r}_1 \, f_{12} \\
&= V\beta_1 + 2\Omega\beta_{\Omega 2}
\end{aligned} \tag{7.9}$$

The last equality defines the new cluster integral

$$2! \, \beta_{\Omega 2} = \int_0^\infty dz_2 \int d\mathbf{r}_1 \, f_{12} \tag{7.9'}$$

The integral (7.9) splits into two contributions: one proportional to the volume which is the usual cluster integral and another which comes from the region in which at least one of the molecules out of the volume while their distance remains bounded by the range of interaction. This second term is clearly proportional to the surface area.

Separating in a systematic way volume and surface contributions, Bellemans obtains the following expression for the surface tension

$$\frac{\sigma}{kT} = - \sum_2^\infty \beta_{\Omega k} C^k \tag{7.10}$$

This is clearly the surface analogue of the equation of state (7.4). The irreducible surface cluster integrals $\beta_{\Omega k}$ are defined in a way similar to (7.5).

References p. 162–163

As an example, Bellemans has calculated the surface tension of a hard-sphere gas of diameter D. He obtains*

$$\frac{\sigma}{DkT} = -0.1875\, bC^2 - 0.1995\, b^2C^3 \ldots \tag{7.11}$$

where b is the second virial coefficient of a hard-sphere gas $(= 2\pi D^3/3)$. As could be expected the surface tension is *negative* and the concentration of the spheres is increased near the surface.

Similar expressions may be given for dilute solutions. For example, we may consider a dilute solution of a rigid spherical polymer of diameter D. One then finds

$$\frac{\sigma - \sigma_0}{DkT} = \tfrac{1}{2}(C + 0.625\, bC^2 + 0.2259\, b^2C^3 + \ldots) \tag{7.12}$$

where σ_0 is the surface tension of the pure solvent.

If we compare Bellemans' theory with the Kirkwood-Buff calculations summarized in section 5, we may say that it retains the first assumption $(n_g^{(1)} = 0)$ which is certainly satisfied far from the critical point, but makes no use of the second (homogeneity of the liquid) till the phase separation. On the contrary, the adsorption and the behavior of the pressure tensor are calculated from the theory and are shown to behave in a physically reasonable way.

It may be hoped that at least in some cases series like (7.10) may be summed exactly and compact expressions which are valid for the condensed state may be obtained.

It may also be expected that the experimental investigation of surface tension using Bellemans' expressions may give rise to a new method for the determination of the size and form of dissolved polymer molecules.

8. MIXTURES

In this section we would like to discuss briefly the relation between intermolecular forces and surface tension for mixtures. On one side this is an even more complicated problem than the evaluation of surface tension for pure liquids because we have now to take account of the *adsorption in the surface phase*. On the other hand we are then primarily interested in the *change* of the surface tension with composition and not in absolute evaluations. This greatly simplifies the problem. The situation is rather similar to that in the volume properties of liquid mixtures.

---

* The first term in (7.11) had been obtained before by Buff. We want also to mention that the first applications of diagram techniques to surface tension problems may be formed in a paper by BUFF AND STILLINGER[22].

While the theory of liquids is still in an unsatisfactory stage, the theory of mixtures has made great progress in recent years[3]. Many unexpected phenomena have been predicted and then experimentally tested.

We would like to give a short account of the theory for molecule interacting through central forces of the type (2.12), (2.13). In a binary mixture A, B we have then to consider three interaction laws

$$\varepsilon_{ij} = \varepsilon_{ij}{}^{\times}\varphi(r/r_{ij}{}^{\times}) \tag{8.1}$$

If we have

$$\varepsilon_{AA}{}^{\times} = \varepsilon_{AB}{}^{\times} = \varepsilon_{BB}{}^{\times}, \quad r_{AA}{}^{\times} = r_{AB}{}^{\times} = r_{BB}{}^{\times} \tag{8.2}$$

the intermolecular forces would be the same and we would expect a surface tension σ identical to that of the pure compounds (we neglect all quantum effects)

$$\sigma = \sigma_A = \sigma_B \tag{8.3}$$

However in general the parameters $\varepsilon_{ij}{}^{\times}$, $r_{ij}{}^{\times}$ are different and we have an 'excess' surface tension

$$\sigma^E = \sigma - x_A\sigma_A - x_B\sigma_B \tag{8.4}$$

different from zero.

Some features in the variation of surface tension with composition may be understood by simple qualitative arguments. For example, there is a close relation between the sign of the excess surface tension and the sign of the excess free energy. The excess free energy is positive if the vapor pressure is higher than that of a perfect solution ('positive' deviations from ideality) and negative in the opposite case (for more details see Ref. 3). Now the general rule is: *the excess free energy and the excess surface tension have opposite signs.* This is simply due to the fact that the surface phase, being less dense, is always nearer to a perfect solution than the volume phase (see for more details Refs. 1, 18).

However, to obtain more quantitative results we have to consider more closely the intermolecular forces.

We may characterize the difference in the scale factors by the three dimensionless quantities:

$$\delta = \frac{\varepsilon_{BB}{}^{\times} - \varepsilon_{AA}{}^{\times}}{\varepsilon_{AA}{}^{\times}}$$

$$\theta = (\varepsilon_{AB}{}^{\times} - \tfrac{1}{2}\varepsilon_{AA}{}^{\times} - \tfrac{1}{2}\varepsilon_{BB}{}^{\times})/\varepsilon_{AA}{}^{\times} \tag{8.5}$$

$$\varrho = (r_{BB}{}^{\times} - r_{AA}{}^{\times})/r_{AA}{}^{\times}$$

(We suppose that $r_{AB}{}^{\times} = \tfrac{1}{2}(r_{AA}{}^{\times} + r_{BB}{}^{\times})$.) The excess surface tension may therefore be developed as a series in δ, θ, ϱ.

This has been done up to second order terms by ENGLERT-CHWOLES AND

PRIGOGINE[18]. Two steps are necessary: In the first adsorption is neglected. We then obtain the so-called *dynamical* surface tension σ_{dyn} in which the composition of the surface phase is identical to that of the solution. This dynamical surface tension is given by a formula similar to (3.1)

$$\sigma_{dyn} = \frac{<\varepsilon^\times>}{<r^\times>^2} \tilde{\sigma} (<\tilde{T}>) \tag{8.6}$$

where $<\varepsilon^\times>$ and $<r^\times>$ are composition dependent average values of the scale factors $\varepsilon^\times$ and $r^\times$. Similarly

$$<\tilde{T}> = \frac{kT}{<\varepsilon^\times>} \tag{8.7}$$

is a composition dependent average reduced temperature. In other words, the mixture is treated in this method, called the *average potential theory*, essentially as a pure liquid but with composition dependent interaction parameters.

   In a second step the decrease of surface tension due to adsorption is calculated. If terms up to second order in ϱ, θ, δ are taken into account, one obtains

$$\sigma = \sigma_{dyn} - \tfrac{1}{2}x_A x_B \frac{\omega_A^0}{kT} \left(\frac{\partial \sigma_{dyn}}{\partial x_A}\right)^2 \tag{8.8}$$

where ω_A^0 is the surface occupied per molecule of the pure compound A. Note that

$$\sigma \leq \sigma_{dyn} \tag{8.9}$$

corresponding to the lowering of the surface tension by absorption. One obtains in this way

$$
\begin{aligned}
\frac{\sigma^E}{x_A x_B} = {} & \sigma_A \left(-\frac{23}{2}\varrho^2 - \varrho^\delta\right) \\
& + \left(\sigma_A - T\frac{d\sigma_A}{dT}\right)(2\theta - 18\varrho^2 - 4\theta\delta x_B + 2\varrho\delta) \\
& + \tfrac{1}{2}T^2 \frac{d^2\sigma_A}{dT^2}(-\delta^2 + 4\theta\delta x_B + 4\theta^2 x_A x_B) \\
& - \tfrac{1}{2}\frac{\omega_A^0}{kT}\left[\left(\sigma_A - T\frac{d\sigma_A}{dT}\right)[\delta + 2\theta(x_A - x_B)] - 2\varrho\sigma_A\right]^2
\end{aligned}
\tag{8.10}
$$

This expression contains only the properties of the pure compound A (σ_A, $d\sigma_A/dT$, $d^2\sigma_A/dT^2$, ω_A^0) as well as the differences in sizes and in interaction (ϱ, θ, δ). For spherical non polar molecules one often finds

$$(\varepsilon_{AB}^\times)^2 \simeq \varepsilon_{AA}^\times \varepsilon_{BB}^\times ; \tag{8.11}$$

therefore (see (8.5))

$$\theta = \sqrt{1+\delta^2} - \tfrac{1}{2}(1 + \delta) \cong - \frac{\delta^2}{8} \qquad (8.12)$$

We are then left only with two parameters δ and ϱ which may be determined by measures on the pure compound A and B (for example by measurements of the equation of state for dilute gases). Therefore an absolute prediction of the surface tension becomes possible. The results for four mixtures are summarized in Table II. The agreement is very satisfactory.

TABLE II

VERIFICATION OF FORMULA (8.10)

$(T = 293°\ K,\ x_A = x_B = 0.5)$

system	δ	ϱ	σ_{abs}^E	σ_{calc}^E
CCl_4—C_6H_{12} (cyclohexane)	0.00	0.033	−0.54	−0.42
C_6H_{12}—$C(CH_3)_4$	−0.23	0.00	−1.50	−1.8
CCl_4—$C(CH_3)_4$	−0.23	0.042	−2.55	−2.9
C_6H_6—$C(CH_3)_4$	−0.34	0.087	−4.3	−3.6

9. CONCLUSION

In spite of the constant progress in equilibrium statistical mechanics new methods are badly needed. Since Gibbs, equilibrium statistical mechanics belongs to the field of applied mathematics: there is no doubt about the quantities which have to be evaluated. The question is 'only' how? Here one is faced with the problem that the basic quantities are highly multiple integrals, practically infinitely multiple integrals. This defines a new limiting process for which no adequate mathematical tool still exists.

REFERENCES

1 See *e.g.* R. DEFAY AND I. PRIGOGINE, *Tension Superficielle et Adsorption*, Desoer, Liège, and Dunod, Paris, 1951; an English translation is in preparation. This monograph contains a very detailed treatment of the thermodynamics of surfaces.
2 T. HILL, *Statistical Mechanics*, McGraw-Hill, New York, 1956.
3 I. PRIGOGINE, A. BELLEMANS AND V. MATHOT, *The Molecular Theory of Solutions*, North Holland Publ. Co. Amsterdam, and Interscience, New York, 1957.
4 See *e.g.* H. S. GREEN, *Kinetic Theory of Liquids*, North Holland Publ. Co., Amsterdam, and Interscience, New York.
5 E. A. GUGGENHEIM, *J. Chem. Phys.*, 13 (1945) 253.
6 J. E. LENNARD-JONES AND J. CORNER, *Trans. Faraday Soc.*, 36 (1940) 1156.
7 J. CORNER, *Trans. Faraday Soc.*, 44 (1948) 1036.
8 I. PRIGOGINE AND L. SARAGA, *J. Chim. Phys.*, 49 (1952) 399.
9 S. ONO, *Mem. Fac. Eng., Kyushu Univ.*, 20 (1947) 195.

10 F. P. Buff, *Adv. Chem. Ser.*, 33 (1961) 340.

11 J. C. Kirkwood and F. P. Buff, *J. Chem. Phys.*, 17 (1949) 338.

12 I. Prigogine and R. Defay, *Bull. Soc. Chim. Belg.*, 59 (1950) 255.

13 D. Atack and O. K. Rice, *Disc. Faraday Soc.*, 15 (1953) 210.

14 J. W. Cohen and J. E. Hilliard, *J. Chem. Phys.*, 28 (1958) 258.

15 A. Bellemans, *Bull. Soc. Chim. Belg.*, 70 (1961) 58.

16 A. Bellemans, *Physica*, 28 (1962) 493.

17 F. H. Stillinger and F. P. Buff, *J. Chem. Phys.*, 37 (1962) 1.

18 A. Englert-Chwoles and I. Prigogine, *J. Chim. Phys.*, 55 (1958) 16.

19 A. Harasima, *Adv. Chem. Phys.*, Vol. I, Interscience, New York, 1958, p. 203.

20 E. A. Guggenheim, *Mixtures*, Oxford Univ. Press, London, 1952, Ch. IV.

21 R. H. Fowler, *Statistical Mechanics*, Cambridge Univ. Press, London, 1956.

22 F. P. Buff and F. H. Stillinger, *J. Chem. Phys.*, 25 (1956) 312.

Surface Effects in Non-Spherical Motions
of Small Cavities

T. BROOKE BENJAMIN

*Department of Engineering, University of Cambridge,
Cambridge, England*

ABSTRACT

This paper is mainly concerned with the effects of quasi-elastic and quasi-viscous behaviour of interfacial films on the shape oscillations of small gas bubbles in liquids. Some experimental observations which stimulated interest in this topic are recalled, and then the general problem of representing the mechanical properties of surface films is discussed. Criteria of the importance of various film properties during cavity vibrations are derived, and it is shown that in many physical examples, the principal effect of a film is to make the cavity surface incompressible with the result that increased damping occurs through viscous dissipation in an adjoining boundary layer within the liquid rather than through quasi-viscous dissipation in the film itself. In the final section of the paper the non-spherical oscillations of a cavity with an incompressible surface are considered and an expression for the rate of damping is obtained.

I. INTRODUCTION

The aim of this contribution to the Symposium is to draw attention to a practical aspect of cavity dynamics which has been little studied so far, yet which appears to have an important bearing on several interesting phenomena. The subject is the rheology of the liquid/gas interface as a factor in the oscillations of a small cavity about spherical shape, and in particular the effects of surface elasticity and surface viscosity on the damping of such oscillations will be discussed. The original stimulus for the theoretical studies to be reported was an experiment made by STRASBERG AND BENJAMIN[1] in which the response of small air bubble to sound waves in water was observed, and in which vigorous shape oscillations appeared to be generated as the result of instability of the radial motions forced by the symmetric sound field. The experiment will be described in section 2 together with a theory proposed by BENJAMIN AND STRASBERG[2] which, in its original form, relates to a bubble with an ideal free surface subject to constant surface tension; its failure to account quantitatively for the experimental observations was a convincing indication that surface effects of the kind now in question were significant. Non-spherical oscillations excited by sound, either directly by non-uniform sound fields or indirectly as in the experiment[1], provide the main scope for present ideas, but other applications come readily to mind. For instance, surface effects may well have an important rôle in the instability of a cavitation bubble during its catastrophic collapse[3, 4], even though the radial motion is unlikely to be influenced significantly by them.

A related property of small bubbles which is well known to be attributable to surface effects is their anomalous rate of rise through a liquid. It has often been observed[5, 6] that the drag of a very small bubble has the value appropriate to a rigid sphere and is thus 50% larger than the drag of an ideal bubble across whose surface the viscous shear stress in the external liquid is communicated to the gas inside, which is thereby driven into a circulatory motion. The first reasonable explanation for this phenomenon was due to BOUSSINESQ[7], and in more recent times the problem has been treated very comprehensively by LEVICH[8]. The essential point of the explanation is that contamination by a film of adsorbed material gives the bubble surface a resistance to tangential displacements; and because the effect on the overall motion increases rapidly with decreasing size, very small bubbles are made effectively rigid even by exceeding small amounts of contaminant per unit area. As will be explained presently, however, there is still some controversy regarding the alternative mechanisms which could provide this resistance.

Another well-known phenomenon dependent on surface effects, and closely related to the present main topic, is the rapid damping of capillary ripples as they are transmitted along a horizontal liquid surface contaminated by an adsorbed film. The remarkable smoothing effect of oil spread thinly over a water surface agitated by wind was first observed scientifically by BENJAMIN FRANKLIN about two centuries ago, having been known to mariners since antiquity*. REYNOLDS was the first to formulate an explanation in terms of the mechanical properties of a contaminated surface, and the phenomenon was studied extensively by RAYLEIGH. A brief account of this early theoretical work is to be found in the text-book by LAMB (Ref. 9, p. 631), and again the most comprehensive available treatment is due to LEVICH[8]. In the last decade or so considerable progress has been made in research on several problems concerned with the rheology of fluid interfaces, notably certain problems with importance in chemical engineering, and reference may be made to the review by SCRIVEN AND STERNLING[10] for a succinct account of the whole subject.

---

* But apparently it was, and still is, commonly misconceived by them. Oil has negligible calming effect on sea waves longer than about a foot, although its effect on the small-scale roughness of the sea surface gives a deceptive impression of the whole wave spectrum being moderated.

References p. 180

Broadly speaking, two types of theory have been applied to the interpretation of hydrodynamical phenomena dependent on interfacial effects. Regarding the mechanical properties of an interface which need to be specified additionally to the equilibrium surface tension, one type of theory considers them to be 'elastic' in character and the other considers them to be 'viscous'. Since these assigned properties merely represent gross effects of molecular processes which are not yet well understood mechanically, and since interfaces may be observed to exhibit both distinctly elastic and distinctly viscous behaviour under particular experimental conditions [11, 12], there is little *a priori* justification for either theoretical model in favour of the other and the choice ultimately rests on the experimental facts about any particular case. The two may be combined in some way, of course, as was done by OLDROYD [13] whose formulation will be followed in this paper. But theories allowing for visco-elastic properties of an interface would appear to lead to unwarranted complications if taken too far, because the model is still a tentative one and the experimental evidence is generally inadequate to test refined theoretical results. In practical respects the chief advantage of such an approach is to provide, at an early stage of the analysis, a definite basis for comparing the overall consequences of the elastic and viscous properties; thus the physical status of results derived by neglecting one or other group of properties may be clearly defined.

In section 3, after a brief discussion of surface elasticity and viscosity in physical terms, the tensor form of the stress-strain relationship for an arbitrary surface with visco-elastic properties will be considered. The stresses exerted by an interface against the contiguous fluids will be expressed in terms of its deformation from an equilibrium configuration, and hence for the case of a nearly spherical interface the elastic and viscous contributions to these stresses will be compared. In section 4 the exact mathematical problem for shape oscillations of a cavity will be outlined, but this extremely complicated problem will not be tackled directly in this paper. In section 5, however, an explicit expression for the rate of damping will be derived by a simple approximate theory applying to a cavity with an 'incompressible' surface, the physical significance of this result having been established in section 3.

2. 'PARAMETRIC EXCITATION' OF NON-SPHERICAL OSCILLATIONS

In the experiment [1] an air bubble was trapped near the centre of a water-filled sphere resonating acoustically in a radially symmetric mode at 25 kc/sec. The bubble held its position under the action of a Bjerknes force attracting it towards the central antinode of the acoustic vibrations and so balancing the buoyancy force. It was observed that as the sound-pressure amplitude was gradually raised the bubble suddenly began to dart about in erratic fashion, its previous quiescent condition having evidently become an unstable one. The critical sound pressure was found to decrease from about 0.6 to 0.17 atm. as the bubble radius was increased from 2 to 7×10^{-3} cm. This behaviour is accountable to the instability of a spherical surface when it undergoes radial pulsations of sufficient amplitude in response to sound, so that oscillatory departures from spherical shape are excited even when the sound field is approximately uniform throughout the vicinity of the bubble. The excitation has essentially the same kind of mechanism as the instability of the plane free surface of liquid in a vessel which is vibrated vertically (BENJAMIN AND URSELL[14]), and it may be generally classified under the term 'parametric excitation' which is commonly used for analogous phenomena with importance in electronics engineering.

The following is an outline of the theory proposed by BENJAMIN AND STRASBERG[2]. In terms of spherical coordinates (r, θ, ω) the perturbed surface of the pulsating bubble is represented by

$$r = R(t) + a(t)S_n(\theta, \omega),\qquad(2.1)$$

where S_n is a surface harmonic of integral order n $(\geqslant 2)$. The amplitude $|a(t)|$ of the perturbation is assumed to be much smaller than the mean radius $R(t)$, which is here considered to be an arbitrary function of time t, its dependence on the applied sound pressure being left implicit. Supposing that the liquid has constant density ϱ and zero viscosity, that its motion is irrotational, and that surface tension is a constant γ_0, one obtains the following differential equation for $a(t)$ (cf. PLESSET AND MITCHELL[3]):

$$R\ddot{a} + 3\dot{R}\dot{a} + (n-1)\left\{(n+1)(n+2)\frac{\gamma_0}{\varrho R^2} - \ddot{R}\right\}a = 0.\qquad(2.2)$$

If the radial pulsation is small it will be approximately simple-harmonic, thus $R = R_0(1 - \varepsilon \cos \varkappa t)$ with $|\varepsilon| \ll 1$. We now put this expression for R into (2.2), and also put $a = b(1 + \tfrac{3}{2}\varepsilon \cos \varkappa t)$. When terms in ε^2 are neglected, the result is

$$\ddot{b} + [\sigma^2 - \varepsilon\{(n+\tfrac{1}{2})\varkappa^2 - 3\sigma^2\} \cos \varkappa t]b = 0,\qquad(2.3)$$

where

$$\sigma = \left\{(n-1)(n+1)(n+2)\frac{\gamma_0}{\varrho R_0^3}\right\}^{\frac{1}{2}}\qquad(2.4)$$

is the frequency of free vibrations in the nth mode (LAMB[9], p. 475).

Eqn. (2.3) may be reduced to the standard form of Mathieu's equation by obvious transformations. Hence, by reference to the theory of Mathieu's equation (cf. BENJAMIN AND URSELL[14], section 3), it appears that instability in the form of exponentially growing oscillations will occur for sufficiently large ε. In particular,

References p. 180

instability is caused by very small radial pulsations (i.e. ε exceptionally small) when $2\sigma/\varkappa \doteqdot 1, 2, 3, \ldots$. The range of the frequency $\varkappa$ for instability is broadest when $\varkappa \doteqdot 2\sigma$, in which case the solution of (2.3) has the form

$$b = e^{kt} \times \text{(periodic function with frequency } \tfrac{1}{2}\varkappa).$$

The maximum of k, obtained when $\varkappa$ is tuned to almost exactly 2σ, is approximately

$$k_{\mathrm{m}} = \varepsilon(4n - 1)\sigma. \tag{2.5}$$

For the 'higher classes' of instability for which $2\sigma/\varkappa \doteqdot s \geq 2$, k_{m} is proportional to ε^s, and so these are less likely to be operative when the radial pulsation is very small. (They are also more readily inhibited by viscosity—see below.) The mode $n = 2$, in which the bubble deforms into ellipsoidal form, appeared to be the one most likely to manifest instability under the conditions of the experiment[1].

To account for the effect of variable surface tension on the coupling between the radial and asymmetric motions, though not on the latter itself, we may put $\gamma = \gamma_0 + \gamma_1\varDelta$, where $\varDelta = -2\varepsilon \cos \varkappa t$ is the overall expansion of the bubble surface (see section 3 below). The result corresponding to (2.5) is then

$$k_{\mathrm{m}} = \varepsilon(4n - 1 + 2\gamma_1/\gamma_0)\sigma. \tag{2.6}$$

It is possible that this effect could contribute significantly to the excitation, since under certain conditions of slight contamination γ_1 for a water surface has a magnitude comparable with or even greater than γ_0.

The preceding analysis rests on the assumption that the liquid is inviscid, but for practical applications an estimate of the effect of viscosity is essential. For oscillations at frequency σ we may define a Reynolds number $\mathscr{R} = \sigma R^2/\nu$, where $\nu = \mu/\varrho$ is the kinematic viscosity of the liquid; and if $\mathscr{R}$ is fairly large, which was so in the experiment, the following simple argument is adequate for the present purpose (cf. BENJAMIN AND URSELL[14], section 6).

Suppose that *free* oscillations at frequency σ are damped by viscous dissipation at a rate α, i.e. their amplitude decays according to $\exp(-\alpha t)$. Since in the absence of viscosity the instability causes oscillations at approximately this frequency to be supplied with energy so that their amplitude grows exponentially at a rate k, we may conclude that the condition of instability for a pulsating bubble in a real liquid is

$$k > \alpha \tag{2.7}$$

approximately. This implies that the mechanisms of energy supply and of dissipation are approximately independent, which is a justifiable assumption if k and α are only small fractions of σ. The damping ratio α/σ clearly will be small when $\mathscr{R}$ is large, provided n is not too large so that the effective 'wavelength', $2\pi R/n$, of

References p. 180

the oscillation is not too small. [In the original study made by BENJAMIN AND STRASBERG[2] the instability condition (2.7) was also derived formally from the full equations of motion for a viscous liquid, and the error was seen to be $O(\mathscr{R}^{-\frac{1}{2}})$.]

Considering slowly damped oscillations of a bubble with a perfect free surface, LAMB[9] (p. 641) gave the result

$$\frac{\alpha}{\sigma} = (n + 2)\,(2n + 1)\,\frac{1}{\mathscr{R}}. \tag{2.8}$$

This was used by BENJAMIN AND STRASBERG in an attempt to explain the experimental observations of the stability limit, but no satisfactory agreement was achieved. It was therefore concluded that the theoretical predictions for a perfect free surface were probably irrelevant, and that the observed phenomenon was significantly dependent on the kind of surface effects discussed in this paper. Admittedly the experimental findings have still not been afforded a satisfactory quantitative interpretation by a modified theory, but at least they have indicated that the calculation of the damping rate α on a more realistic basis is an essential first step towards an understanding of small-bubble behaviour of the kind demonstrated.

As a final comment on the experiment the following conjecture may be of interest. Even after a very gradual approach to the critical condition, the manifestation of instability was often remarkably violent, resulting in the rapid projection of the bubble over distances many times its diameter; and if no additional physical factor is allowed, it seems hardly adequate to account for this behaviour as the outcome of instability of the original spherical form to small perturbations. However, the growth of non-spherical oscillations to fairly large size may have caused a contaminating film over the bubble surface to be broken up or dissolved, and the removal of its restraining influence may then have precipitated a more vigorous transfer of energy to the asymmetric motion, so that the instability became catastrophic.

3. MECHANICAL MODELS FOR INTERFACES

It has already been noted in section 1 that the mechanical properties of surface films admit no simple general description and that the alternative models proposed by different writers may all be considered potentially useful for *ad hoc* application to particular physical problems. The composition of films forming naturally on the surfaces of bubbles in water is likely to vary greatly under typical conditions in a fluid-dynamics laboratory, and the actual surface properties of very small bubbles, such as exhibit anomalous drag, is largely a matter of conjecture; but this aspect of the subject is beyond the scope of this paper. The only point worth emphasizing in this connection is that macroscopic surface properties due to even extremely thin contaminating films like dispersed monolayers[11], such as are almost impossible to eliminate in practice, can profoundly affect wave motions with length scales less than about a centimetre.

In his original treatment of the rising-bubble problem, BOUSSINESQ[7] proposed that, in addition to its equilibrium tension, the contaminating film suffers stresses proportional to *rates of strain*; accordingly the resistance of the film to tangential deformations is characterized by two coefficients of 'surface viscosity', one respective to shear and the other to expansion of the surface. BOUSSINESQ's formulation has been generalized by SCRIVEN[15] so as to apply to an arbitrary moving surface. On the other hand, following REYNOLDS and RAYLEIGH, one may suppose the additional stresses to be proportional to the actual (static) strains, thus assigning *elastic* properties to the surface. This approach was adopted by LEVICH[8] in his treatment of the rising bubble problem, and he presented arguments supporting his model in favour of BOUSSINESQ's in some specific physical examples. An effect also included in his analysis is the variation of surface tension due to local changes in a soluble film when material is tranferred into or out of solution. In the present problem, however, there is reason to believe this effect is insignificant, even for bubbles whose drag may depend on it. A criterion of its importance is the relaxation time for solute diffusion in comparison with the period of the oscillations, and some rough estimates have indicated that usually the former greatly exceeds the latter.

The classical idea of surface elasticity as represented by the Plateau-Marangoni-Gibbs effect[10], and its role in wave damping, may be summarized as follows (*cf.* LAMB[9], p. 361). As is well known, the addition of thin films of certain substances to liquid surfaces lowers the overall surface tension. (This is why a contaminating film spreads spontaneously over a previously clean surface.) Moreover, the local surface tension varies inversely with the concentration of the contaminant; and so, after a film has become fully spread over a surface of fixed total area, any local expansion or contraction of the film will give rise to forces opposing the change. Thus the film tends to behave like an incompressible membrane, though having a resistance to bending provided in the familiar way by the mean surface tension. If the surface bounds a liquid with small viscosity, wave motions in the absence of the contamination will be approximately irrotational (LAMB[9], section 348), and for any such motion the material surface is necessarily expanded in the wavetroughs and compressed at the crests. A surface film providing resistance to such strains will therefore generate vorticity in the liquid; an oscillating boundary layer of thickness $O(\nu/\sigma)^{\frac{1}{2}}$ will in fact be created just inside the liquid, and viscous dissipation in this layer may increase the rate of damping of the waves far above its value for a clean surface. A contaminated surface may also exhibit some elastic resistance to shearing in its plane, although the respective elasticity modulus is generally much smaller than the compression modulus.

The following mathematical representation of interfacial properties follows closely the work of OLDROYD[13], and is also akin to the treatments by SCRIVEN[15] and GOODRICH[16]. The properties of a contaminating film will be likened to those of a thin 'membrane-shell' of elastico-viscous material which, before deformation, is under a uniform tension γ_0, i.e. the equilibrium surface tension. It is assumed that the deformation leaves the total area of the film unchanged to first order in the magnitude of the perturbation, this being so of course during the shape oscillations of a bubble about spherical form (note that the potential energy of such oscillations is γ_0 times the increase in area, so that this increase must be a second-order quantity). Upon deformation of the film two sets of additional forces arise, which are assumed to be linearly independent: elastic stress-resultants proportional to strain, and viscous stress-resultants proportional to rate of strain. Thus, in effect, the film is represented as a primarily elastic body with supplementary viscous properties (i.e. a 'Voigt body'). The means for representing other types of linear rheological behaviour has been suggested by OLDROYD, but among the possible *simple* models the present one seems to be the most realistic for our particular application.

We consider a system of curvilinear coordinates x^i convected with the film and such that $x^3 = 0$ defines its surface Σ. The metric tensor $a_{\alpha\beta}$ for the surface is given by

$$(ds)^2 = a_{\alpha\beta} \, dx^\alpha \, dx^\beta \quad (\alpha = 1, 2; \; \beta = 1, 2), \tag{3.1}$$

where ds is the distance between adjacent points on Σ. It is supposed that the film is perturbed from a state of equilibrium, and the metric tensor for the undeformed surface Σ_0 is denoted by $A_{\alpha\beta}$ (strictly speaking, this is the component in Σ_0 of a three-dimensional metric tensor referred to the coordinate system x^i, but presently it will be admissible as a first-order approximation to refer $A_{\alpha\beta}$ and various other tensors to surface coordinates in Σ_0). The surface strain tensor $e_{\alpha\beta}$ is given by

$$(ds)^2 - (ds)_0^2 = 2e_{\alpha\beta} \, dx^\alpha \, dx^\beta \tag{3.2}$$

where $(ds)_0$ is the length element on Σ_0, and so we have $e_{\alpha\beta} = \frac{1}{2}(a_{\alpha\beta} - A_{\alpha\beta})$. Next, considering

$$D(ds)^2/Dt = 2f_{\alpha\beta} \, dx^\alpha \, dx^\beta, \tag{3.3}$$

we see that the rate-of-strain tensor is $f_{\alpha\beta} = \frac{1}{2}Da_{\alpha\beta}/Dt$. Since there is no slipping between the film and the liquid, $e_{\alpha\beta}$ and $f_{\alpha\beta}$ correspond to the components in the surface Σ of the three-dimensional strain and rate-of-strain tensors for the liquid (i.e. to e_{ij} and f_{ij} with $i, j = 1$ and 2 only); hence they can at once be found when the displacements X_i and velocities DX_i/Dt of the liquid are specified. Assuming that the perturbation from Σ_0 is small, we have that $e_{\alpha\beta}$ and $f_{\alpha\beta}$ are of first-order smallness, and since Σ_0 is assumed to be fixed in space we can, when required, replace the total time derivative D/Dt by $\partial/\partial t$ as a first-order approximation.

The quasi-elastic forces are considered first, being expressed as additions to the uniform tension $\gamma_0 a_{\alpha\beta}$. According to Hook's law in the form used in membrane theory[17], the stress-resultant tensor (*i.e.* stress averaged over film thickness) is

$$N_{\alpha\beta} = \gamma_0 a_{\alpha\beta} + (\gamma_1 - \gamma_2)\Delta a_{\alpha\beta} + 2\gamma_2 e_{\alpha\beta}, \tag{3.4}$$

where the invariant $\Delta = e_\alpha^\alpha$ is the surface expansion. Here γ_1 and γ_2 are elasticity coefficients, the first being in effect a modulus of surface dilatation and the second a modulus of surface shear. [Note that for the analogous elastic shell,

$$\gamma_1 = Eh/2(1 - \sigma) \quad \text{and} \quad \gamma_2 = Gh = Eh/2(1 + \sigma),$$

where E is Young's modulus and G the rigidity modulus, h is the shell thickness, and σ is Poisson's ratio. Note also that as a first-order approximation to the *second* term in (3.4) $a_{\alpha\beta}$ may be replaced by $A_{\alpha\beta}$ and the coordinate system may be replaced by one in Σ_0.]

According to our assumption of elastico-viscous behaviour in the manner of a Voight body, a viscous stress-resultant linearly dependent on rate of strain may simply be added to (3.4) in order to give the total $N_{\alpha\beta}$. This component takes the form

$$(\eta_1 - \eta_2)f_\lambda^\lambda a_{\alpha\beta} + 2\eta_2 f_{\alpha\beta} \doteqdot (\eta_1 - \eta_2)\frac{\partial\Delta}{\partial t} A_{\alpha\beta} + 2\eta_2 \frac{\partial e_{\alpha\beta}}{\partial t}, \tag{3.5}$$

where η_1 and η_2 are the surface-viscosity coefficients analogous to γ_1 and γ_2. The first-order approximation on the right-hand side is justified by the fact that Σ_0 is at rest.

It must be emphasized that the expressions (3.4) and (3.5) rest on the same basic assumptions as membrane theory and imply that the external loading of the film will be borne virtually entirely by the tension γ_0 and the stress-resultants; that is, stress couples and shear forces in a direction normal to the film are neglected so that a plane film, for instance, has no bending stiffness other than that provided by the equilibrium tension. This approximation seems amply justified, however, for all but exceptionally thick films, the reason being that in their physical forms the external force resultants due to the latter effects will, in comparison with those kept in the analysis, have an additional factor h^2 and will depend on higher derivatives of the surface displacement and velocity. This would appear to be so however these effects arise. On this point, therefore, we must dispute the analytical formulation of film behaviour made by GOODRICH[16], which included a component equivalent to a term $\eta_0 \partial a_{\alpha\beta}/\partial t$ added to (3.5).

The stress system generated in the deformed film must be balanced by the stresses exerted against it by the contiguous fluids, and we now consider the action of a viscous liquid on one side ($x^3 > 0$) and an inviscid gas at constant pressure P_0 on the other. The inertia of the film will be neglected, as is obviously well justified by its extreme thinness compared with the scale of the liquid motion. Expressions for the liquid stresses in terms of $N_{\alpha\beta}$ are directly available from membrane theory (GREEN AND ZERNA[17], Ch. 12; cf. also SCRIVEN[15], p. 104). First, the direct stress normal to the film is given by

$$p = - P_0 - N^{\alpha\beta} b_{\alpha\beta}, \tag{3.6}$$

where $b_{\alpha\beta}$ is the second fundamental form for the surface Σ (the corresponding form for Σ_0 will be denoted by $B_{\alpha\beta}$). Substituting (3.4) with the viscous component (3.5) added, and making approximations to the first order in small quantities, we get from (3.6)

$$p = - P_0 - 2\gamma_0 H - 2\{(\gamma_1 - \gamma_2) + (\eta_1 - \eta_2)\partial/\partial t\} \Delta H_0 \\ - 2(\gamma_2 + \eta_2 \partial/\partial t)e^{\alpha\beta}B_{\alpha\beta}, \tag{3.7}$$

where $H = \tfrac{1}{2}a^{\alpha\beta}b_{\alpha\beta}$ is the mean curvature of the perturbed surface Σ, and $H_0 = \tfrac{1}{2}A^{\alpha\beta}B_{\alpha\beta}$ is the mean curvature of Σ_0. In the present physical problem Σ_0 is spherical, so that $B_{12} = 0$ and, in their physical forms, both principal curvatures are equal to $-1/R$. Hence we may write $2H = 2/R + \delta$, where δ is the curvature perturbation. Thus finally the physical form of p is found to be

$$p = - P_0 + \gamma_0 \left(\frac{2}{R} + \delta\right) + \frac{2}{R}\left\{\gamma_1 \Delta + \eta_1 \dot{\Delta}\right\}. \tag{3.8}$$

It may be noted incidentally that for the surface described by (2.1), R now being assumed constant, the curvature perturbation is (LAMB[9], p. 475)

$$\delta = (n - 1)(n + 2)\frac{aS_n}{R^2}, \tag{3.9}$$

and clearly Δ and $\dot{\Delta}$ are of first order in a, being readily expressible in terms of the tangential displacements of the film (see section 5).

There remain two components of shear stress exerted against Σ by the liquid. These are given by

$$\tau^{\alpha} = - N^{\alpha\beta}{}_{,\beta}. \tag{3.10}$$

(Here the comma denotes covariant differentiation along Σ.) Substituting (3.4) with (3.5) added and remembering that the covariant derivatives of $a_{\alpha\beta}$ are zero, one gets from (3.10)

References p. 180

$$\tau^\alpha = -\{(\gamma_1 - \gamma_2)\varDelta_{,\beta} + (\eta_1 - \eta_2)\dot{\varDelta}_{,\beta}\}a^{\alpha\beta} - 2(\gamma_2 e^{\alpha\beta}{}_{,\beta} + \eta_2 \dot{e}^{\alpha\beta}{}_{,\beta}). \quad (3.11)$$

Consistently with the overall first-order approximation, the evaluation of this expression can be simplified by performing the differentiations with respect to coordinates in Σ_0. Note also that $\varDelta_{,\beta}$ is the same as $\partial\varDelta/\partial x_\beta$.

For a purely elastic surface for which γ_2 is negligible in comparison with γ_1, as is commonly the case, (3.11) reduces to

$$\tau = \gamma_1 \operatorname{grad}_s \varDelta, \quad (3.12)$$

where $\operatorname{grad}_s \equiv a^{\alpha\beta}\partial/\partial x_\beta$ denotes the surface gradient. This reproduces a fairly well-known result which is noted, for instance, in the text-book by LANDAU AND LIFSHITZ[18] (section 62). It gives precise expression to the classical concept of surface elasticity as discussed earlier.

Though we now have the means of formulating realistic boundary conditions for the problem of vibrating bubbles, this problem still presents a formidable task of analysis. The exact form of the problem will be summarized in the next section of this paper, but there we shall leave it. The more specific object of the rest of the paper is to estimate the overall influence of the surface properties represented above, and to secure a basis for an approximate calculation of the damping rate for non-spherical oscillations.

As has already been mentioned, γ_2 is usually very much smaller than γ_1 for thin films such as monolayers[11]. Typically γ_1 is of the same order of magnitude as the equilibrium surface tension γ_0, while γ_2 is two orders of magnitude smaller. Accordingly, since shape oscillations of a cavity will tend to produce dilatational and shearing strains of comparable magnitude in the surface, γ_2 may reasonably be neglected. (But see the remarks at the end of section 4 about a 'second class' of oscillations.)

Suppose now that during shape oscillations at frequency σ the surface undergoes tangential displacements of a representative magnitude V/σ, where V is the magnitude of the tangential velocities. Accordingly, the surface gradient of the expansion $\varDelta$ will be at most $O(k^2V/\sigma)$, where $k = O(n/R)$ is the 'wave-number' of the oscillations (i.e. the reciprocal length scale for spatial variations of the displacements); and we may denote its actual magnitude by $O(sk^2V/\sigma)$, where s is a dimensionless coefficient measuring the effectiveness of the displacements in producing expansions and contractions of the surface film. Hence, according to (3.12), the tangential stresses due to elasticity of the film are $O(s\gamma_1 n^2V/\sigma R^2)$. But these stresses must be balanced by viscous stresses in the liquid, and at large Reynolds number $\mathscr{R}$ these will be $O\{\mu V(\sigma/\nu)^{\frac12}\}$ since the main effects of viscosity will be confined to an oscillating boundary layer of thickness $O(\nu/\sigma)^{\frac12}$. (Note that the ratio of the thickness $(\nu/\sigma)^{\frac12}$ to the cavity radius R is $\mathscr{R}^{-\frac12}$.) Equating these two order-of-magnitude estimates for the stresses, we get

$$s = O \left\{ \frac{\varrho R^2 (\sigma^3 \nu)^{\frac{1}{2}}}{n^2 \gamma_1} \right\}.$$

By equation (2.4) we also have $\sigma^2 = O(n^3 \gamma_0 / \varrho R^3)$, hence

$$s = O \left(\frac{\gamma_0}{\gamma_1} \cdot \frac{n}{\mathscr{R}^{\frac{1}{2}}} \right). \tag{3.13}$$

It is clear that if $s \ll 1$ the film behaves virtually as if it were incompressible; that is, only very small dilatations are forced by the viscous stresses. And we see from (3.12) that, provided $\gamma_1/\gamma_0 = O(1)$ and n is not too large, this condition is obtained at large Reynolds numbers. In section 5 a large-$\mathscr{R}$ approximation to the damping rate will be derived, and the present result establishes the physical basis for our assumption that $\Delta = 0$, and therefore $\dot{\Delta} = 0$, during the oscillations. (Note incidentally that the interpretation of a condition $s \gg 1$ given by (3.12), for instance when $\gamma_1 \to 0$, is that the oscillating boundary layer must be absent, so that the liquid motion is irrotational right up to the (free) surface.)

A film undergoing no expansion or contraction by virtue of its elastic stiffness may still be subject to shearing during an oscillation, and accordingly we must now estimate the effect of viscous resistance to shearing as represented by the coefficient η_2. It appears that shape oscillations of a cavity at larger Reynolds number have the property that the material surface suffers no rotation about a normal axis (this follows fairly obviously from the fact that the vorticity vector in the boundary layer is tangential to the surface, the normal component being zero as in the irrotational motion outside the boundary layer). Hence the question naturally arises whether or not a condition of both zero expansion and zero rotation of a surface film implies that no first-order stress whatever is exerted externally other than that due to the equilibrium tension, as is well known to be the case for a perturbed plane shell. Consideration of the general formula (3.11), shows, however, that this result does not hold for a perturbed spherical shell since it depends on the additional condition, not satisfied in this case, that the total (Gaussian) curvature of the undeformed surface should be zero (cf. SCRIVEN[15]). Thus, even if $\Delta = 0$, shear stresses are exerted against the liquid during shape oscillations of a cavity, and indeed it is a fairly simple matter to show that the physical components of these stresses in the spherical-coordinate directions (θ, ω) are both equal to $2\eta_2 v / R^2$, where v is the velocity in the θ-direction. The effect on the overall motion may be estimated as before by considering the ratio of the magnitude of these stresses to the magnitude of the viscous stresses in the liquid. This ratio is found to be

$$q = O \left(\frac{\eta_2}{R\mu} \cdot \frac{n^2}{\mathscr{R}^{\frac{1}{2}}} \right), \tag{3.14}$$

and clearly if $q \ll 1$ the effect is negligible. Even if $q = O(1)$, the surface will remain effectively incompressible provided $s \ll 1$, but in this case viscous dissipation in the film itself would be comparable with the dissipation in the liquid boundary layer, so that the former could not be ignored in estimating the damping rate.

Film viscosity will in fact be neglected in the simplified calculation of section 5, and according to (3.14) the additional physical condition which justifies this approximation is roughly that $\eta_2/R\mu$ is $O(1)$ or less. For many adsorbed monolayers η_2 is about 10^{-4} g sec^{-1} (Ref. 11). Thus, taking $\mu = 0.01$ g cm^{-1} sec^{-1} for water and $R = 0.01$ cm, for instance, one gets $\eta_2/R\mu = 1$.

4. SUMMARY OF EXACT PROBLEM

A complete analysis of non-spherical vibrations may be made on the following lines. The time dependence of the solution is represented by a factor $\exp(i\sigma t)$ in which σ is complex, its imaginary part being the damping rate. The velocity vector for the motion of the liquid is then expressible in the form (cf. LAMB[9], section 353)

$$\mathbf{u} = \frac{i}{\varrho\mu}\operatorname{grad} P + \mathbf{u}', \tag{4.1}$$

where P, the pressure perturbation, is a harmonic function and $\mathbf{u}'$ is a solution of

$$(\nabla^2 - i\sigma/\nu)\mathbf{u}', \operatorname{div} \mathbf{u}' = 0. \tag{4.2}$$

The displacements of the cavity surface are expressed in terms of a single surface harmonic S_n, the radial component taking the form of the second term in (2.1), and correspondingly the dependence of the velocity components on (θ, ω) is represented in terms of S_n. (The solution of (4.2) is then expressible by Bessel functions of half-integral order.)

Hence the condition $\mathbf{u} \to 0$ for $r \to \infty$ gives a solution $\mathbf{u}$ involving just one arbitrary constant in addition to the arbitrary magnitude of P at $r = R$. The three stress components exerted by the liquid on the cavity surface are then expressed in terms of P and the derivatives of the velocity components evaluated at $r = R$.

Thus far the description of the physical situation involves five unknown quantities, which include the amplitudes of the three components of displacement at the surface of the cavity. But six (linearized) boundary conditions have to be satisfied, namely (i) three kinematical conditions relating the rates of displacement of the surface to the velocity of contiguous fluid particles, (ii) two conditions of shear-stress equilibrium as represented by (3.11), and (iii) a normal-stress condition as

References p. 180

represented by (3.8). Hence, by means of these conditions, elimination of all arbitrary constants in the solution leads to an eigenvalue relationship of the implicit form

$$\sigma = \sigma(R, \varrho, \mu, \gamma_0, \gamma_1, \gamma_2, \eta_1, \eta_2; n). \tag{4.3}$$

As a basis for forming dimensionless parameters it is suitable to introduce the frequency σ_0 of the (undamped) oscillations when viscosity is absent and the cavity has a perfect free surface (*i.e.* the frequency given by (2.4)). The implicit result (4.3) is then seen to be equivalent to

$$\frac{\sigma}{\sigma_0} = f\left(\mathcal{R}, \frac{\gamma_1}{\varrho \sigma_0{}^2 R^3}, \frac{\gamma_2}{\varrho \sigma_0{}^2 R^3}, \frac{\eta_1}{\varrho \sigma_0 R^3}, \frac{\eta_2}{\varrho \sigma_0 R^3}; n\right), \tag{4.4}$$

where $\mathcal{R}$ is the Reynolds number defined earlier and the other quantities within the parentheses are also dimensionless. If the second to fifth of them are zero (*i.e.* the cavity surface is uncontaminated), we know from LAMB's approximate analysis recalled in section 2 that $\sigma/\sigma_0 = 1 + O(\mathcal{R}^{-1})$ as $\mathcal{R} \to \infty$. But from what has been said in section 3 we may anticipate a different result for large $\mathcal{R}$ if the second parameter, say Γ_1, is not zero, even though Γ_1 will not appear explicitly in the first approximation to $(\sigma/\sigma_0) - 1$. For this case the simplified analysis of section 5 will show that $\sigma/\sigma_0 = 1 + O(\mathcal{R}^{-\frac{1}{2}})$ as $\mathcal{R} \to \infty$, and this result is also forthcoming from the exact analysis by formally taking the limit $\mathcal{R} \to \infty$, $\Gamma_1 \neq 0$.

The modes of vibration indicated by the analysis fall into two classes. In the first, which is the one implied in our earlier discussions, the cavity surface undergoes radial displacements as described by equation (2.1) (or equation (5.1) below) and, if $\mathcal{R}$ is large, the liquid motion is approximately irrotational outside a thin boundary layer, within which the term $\mathbf{u}'$ in (4.1) has the same importance as the irrotational component. During vibrations in the second class, the cavity surface remains spherical and undergoes only tangential displacements. Elasticity of the surface film provides the stiffness element for these vibrations, and there are modes for which only its shear resistance is brought into effect. The frequency of vibrations in this second class may be quite high since only liquid in the boundary layer is set in motion, so that the inertia is small at large Reynolds number, but these vibrations appear to be highly damped in most physical examples.

Though straightforward in principle the analysis outlined above is extremely unwieldy, and simple expressions for σ cannot be obtained except by introducing approximations of the asymptotic kind, which are justified when $\mathcal{R}^{\frac{1}{2}}$ may be considered a large parameter. For many practical applications, however, the first approximation obtained more simply as follows may be adequate, particularly if the result is modified to include the damping effect of shear viscosity in an incompressible film.

5. DAMPING OF SHAPE OSCILLATIONS OF CAVITY WITH QUASI-INCOMPRESSIBLE SURFACE

It is supposed that the cavity surface is given by

$$r = R + a(t)S_n(\theta, \omega), \tag{5.1}$$

where R is constant and $a(t)$ represents a slowly damped oscillation at frequency σ. By definition S_n is a solution of

$$\operatorname{cosec} \theta \frac{\partial}{\partial \theta} \left(\sin \theta \frac{\partial S_n}{\partial \theta} \right) + \operatorname{cosec}^2 \theta \frac{\partial^2 S_n}{\partial \omega^2} + n(n+1)S_n = 0. \tag{5.2}$$

In an irrotational fluid motion bounded by the surface (5.1) and extending to infinite radius, the velocity components respective to (r, θ, ω) are

$$u, v, w = \dot{a} \left(\frac{R}{r} \right)^{n+2} \left(S_n, \; -\frac{1}{n+1} \frac{\partial S_n}{\partial \theta}, \; -\frac{1}{n+1} \operatorname{cosec} \theta \frac{\partial S_n}{\partial \omega} \right). \tag{5.3}$$

Hence the tangential velocities on the outer side of the thin boundary layer adjoining the cavity surface are taken to be

$$v_1, w_1 = -\frac{\dot{a}}{n+1} \left(\frac{\partial S_n}{\partial \theta}, \; \operatorname{cosec} \theta \frac{\partial S_n}{\partial \omega} \right). \tag{5.4}$$

The tangential velocities v_2, w_2 at the surface have distributions similar to (5.4) but a different amplitude factor, say A.

Now, the rate of expansion of the material surface is given in general, to the first order in small quantities, by

$$\dot{A} = (\operatorname{div} \mathbf{u} - \partial u / \partial r)_{r=R} = \operatorname{div}_s \mathbf{u}_s - (2u/r)_{r=R}, \tag{5.5}$$

where $\mathbf{u} = (u, v, w)$ and $\mathbf{u}_s = (0, v_2, w_2)$; and in the present case we take $\dot{A} = 0$. We have $u = \dot{a}S_n$ at $r = R$; and hence, substituting the expressions for v_2, w_2 and using (5.2), we readily find from (5.5) that $A = 2\dot{a}/n(n+1)$. It follows that the components $\hat{v} = v_2 - v_1$ and $\hat{w} = w_2 - w_1$ of the velocity difference across the boundary layer are

$$\hat{v}, \hat{w} = \frac{n+2}{n(n+1)} \dot{a} \left(\frac{\partial S_n}{\partial \theta}, \; \operatorname{cosec} \theta \frac{\partial S_n}{\partial \omega} \right). \tag{5.6}$$

By a well-known result for oscillating boundary layers (LANDAU AND LIFSHITZ[18], p. 93), the rate of dissipation per unit area is $\frac{1}{2}(\frac{1}{2}\varrho\mu\sigma)^{\frac{1}{2}} (\hat{v}_0^2 + \hat{w}_0^2)$, where $\hat{v}_0$ and $\hat{w}_0$ are the amplitudes of the orthogonal velocity-difference components. The total rate of dissipation is therefore

$$D = \frac{(n+2)^2}{2n^2(n+1)^2} (\frac{1}{2}\varrho\mu\sigma)^{\frac{1}{2}} R^2 \dot{a}_0^2 I, \tag{5.7}$$

where

$$I = \int_0^\pi \int_0^{2\pi} \left\{ \left(\frac{\partial S_n}{\partial \theta} \right)^2 + \operatorname{cosec}^2 \theta \left(\frac{\partial S_n}{\partial \omega} \right)^2 \right\} \sin \theta \; d\theta \; d\omega.$$

This surface integral may be expressed in a simpler form as follows. Multiply (5.2) by S_n and integrate each term over the complete surface. The first two terms can be integrated by parts, and accordingly one finds that

$$I = n(n + 1)J, \qquad J = \int_0^\pi \int_0^{2\pi} S_n^2 \sin \theta \; d\theta \; d\omega. \tag{5.8}$$

Therefore

$$D = \frac{(n + 2)^2}{2n(n + 1)} \; (\tfrac{1}{2}\varrho\mu\sigma)^{\frac{1}{2}} R^2 \dot{a}_0^2 J. \tag{5.9}$$

The total energy E of the oscillations is most easily found by calculating the (maximum) kinetic energy when $a = 0$, $\dot{a} = \dot{a}_0$. It is

$$E = \frac{1}{2(n + 1)} \; \varrho R^3 \dot{a}_0^2 J. \tag{5.10}$$

Supposing that the oscillations are damped at a rate α, i.e., $a = a_0 e^{-\alpha t} \sin \sigma t$, we have that $D = 2\alpha E$. Hence (5.9) and (5.10) show that

$$\alpha = \frac{(n + 2)^2}{2\sqrt{2}\,n} \cdot \frac{\sigma^{\frac{1}{2}}}{v^{\frac{1}{2}}R} \,,$$

or

$$\frac{\alpha}{\sigma} = \frac{(n + 2)^2}{2\sqrt{2}\,n} \cdot \frac{1}{\mathscr{R}^{\frac{1}{2}}}. \tag{5.11}$$

Comparing this result with the corresponding result (2.8) for a cavity with a free surface, we see that at large Reynolds number incompressibility of the surface results in greatly increased damping. The present and former expressions give comparable values of α when $n = O(\mathscr{R}^{\frac{1}{2}})$, but this interpretation is spurious since neither expression is valid for such large values of n, the present giving $\alpha/\sigma = O(1)$ contrary to assumption. However, if we take the limit $n \to \infty$ while $n/R \to k$, (5.11) recovers the result given by LAMB[9] (p. 632) and LANDAU AND LIFSHITZ[18] (p. 244) for the damping of waves of length $2\pi/k$ on a contaminated *plane* liquid surface. This is to be expected, of course, since for n very large the deformations in the spherical surface become sinusoidal corrugations whose wavelength $2\pi R/n$ is so small in comparison with the radius that the motion is unaffected by the mean curvature.

References p. 180

REFERENCES

1 M. STRASBERG AND T. BROOKE BENJAMIN, Excitation of Oscillations in the Shape of Pulsating Gas Bubbles; Experimental Work. Paper read at *55th Meeting of the Acoust. Soc. Amer.*, Washington, D.C. (1958).

2 T. BROOKE BENJAMIN AND M. STRASBERG, Excitation of Oscillations in the Shape of Pulsating Gas Bubbles; Theoretical Work, Paper read at *55th Meeting of the Acoust. Soc. Amer.*, Washington, D.C. (1958).

3 M. S. PLESSET AND T. P. MITCHELL, On the Stability of the Spherical Shape of a Vapour Cavity in a Liquid, *Quart. Appl. Math.*, 13 (1956) 419.

4 G. BIRKHOFF, *Quart. Appl. Math.*, 12 (1954) 306.

5 G. BIRKHOFF, *Hydrodynamics*, Dover, New York, 1955, p. 34.

6 W. L. HABERMAN AND R. K. MORTON, *David Taylor Model Basin, Rept. no. 802*, 1953.

7 J. BOUSSINESQ, *Ann. Chim. Phys.*, 29 (1913) 349.

8 V. G. LEVICH, *Physico-chemical Hydrodynamics* (in Russian), Moscow, 1952. (See also A. FRUMKIN AND V. G. LEVICH, Effects of Surface-active Substances on Movements at the Boundaries of Liquid Phases, *Russ. J. Phys. Chem.*, 21 (1947) 1183.)

9 H. LAMB, *Hydrodynamics*, Dover, New York, 1945.

10 L. E. SCRIVEN AND C. V. STERNLING, The Marangoni Effects, *Nature*, 187 (1960) 186.

11 J. T. DAVIES AND E. K. RIDEAL, *Interfacial Phenomena*, Academic Press, New York, 1961, Ch. 5.

12 D. W. CRIDDLE, The Viscosity and Elasticity of Interfaces, Ch. 5 in *Rheology*, Vol. 3 (editor F. R. EIRICH), Academic Press, New York, 1960.

13 J. G. OLDROYD, The Effect of Interfacial Stabilizing Films on the Elastic and Viscous Properties of Emulsions, *Proc. Roy. Soc. (London)*, A 232 (1955) 567.

14 T. BROOKE BENJAMIN AND F. URSELL, The Stability of the Plane Free Surface of a Liquid in Vertical Periodic Motion, *Proc. Roy. Soc. (London)*, A 225 (1954) 505.

15 L. E. SCRIVEN, Dynamics of a Fluid Interface, *Chem. Eng. Sci.*, 2 (1960) 98.

16 F. C. GOODRICH, The Mathematical Theory of Capillarity. II, *Proc. Roy. Soc. (London)*, A 260 (1961) 490.

17 A. E. GREEN AND W. ZERNA, *Theoretical Elasticity*, Oxford Univ. Press, London, 1954, Chs. 10 and 12.

18 L. D. LANDAU AND E. M. LIFSHITZ, *Fluid Mechanics*, Pergamon Press, London, 1959.

Subject Index

PRINTED IN THE NETHERLANDS